UPDATED PRINTIN

PHYSICS
A Numerical World View to accompany

PHYSICS
A WORLD VIEW

Larry D. Kirkpatrick
Gerald F. Wheeler
(both of Montana State University)

Saunders College Publishing

Harcourt Brace Jovanovich College Publishers

Fort Worth ■ Philadelphia ■ San Diego ■ New York ■ Orlando ■ Austin
San Antonio ■ Toronto ■ Montreal ■ London ■ Sydney ■ Tokyo

Printed in the United States of America.

Kirkpatrick: Physics: a Numerical World View to accompany PHYSICS: A WORLD VIEW

ISBN 0-03-074476-8

234 066 9876543

Preface

Welcome

We have written *PHYSICS: A Numerical World View* to develop some of the numerical aspects of your study of physics that can be accessed with simple algebra and geometry. The only course in algebra and geometry that you need to have taken is the first year algebra course offered in most high schools.

PHYSICS: A World View is intended as a conceptual view of physics. Many discussions in the text are presented without the underlying mathematics. This supplement takes you one step further into the mathematics that provides the foundation for the physics world view. This manual cannot be used by itself. It assumes you are reading the primary text, *PHYSICS: A World View,* and it relies on the physics covered there.

You will see many sections in the textbook that have the symbol Σ printed to the right of the section heading. This symbol means that some of the ideas discussed in the section are developed further in this supplement. Read the primary text before turning to this manual. The supplement starts where the primary text ends; it makes little attempt to go back over the material.

Why Use Numbers?

In many ways mathematics is the language of physics. While the basic concepts of our world view often originate in our physical descriptions and thus can be expressed in words, it is usually the mathematical manipulations of these concepts that give us powerful insights. In our development of a physics world view, we will see many instances where such mathematical manipulations have generated new physical concepts.

Just as you don't have to have the talent to paint a masterpiece in order to appreciate a great painting, you do not need to be mathematically skilled in order to appreciate the physics world view. However, it often helps to do a few simple calculations while developing an understanding of a basic physical concept. It is in this spirit that we have written this mathematical supplement.

Organization

This manual begins with an introductory chapter on significant digits and units. The rest of the chapters follow the organization of the text. There is a one-to-one correspondence between the titles of the sections in the text and this supplement. In a few cases, extra sections are added to the supplement. The topics in this manual are mostly independent of each other and need not be studied in order.

The sections of this manual contain numerous worked examples and practice problems. The answers to the practice problems are placed in a footnote at the bottom of the page for easy reference. At the end of each chapter, there is an abundance of problems. The more challenging problems are marked with an asterisk. Answers to the odd-numbered problems are given at the end of the manual. Solutions to all the problems are provided in the Instructor's Resource Manual.

Appendix

We have collected the values for many of the commonly used physical constants and physical data in an appendix at the end of the manual. This appendix also includes a list of standard abbreviations, prefixes for the powers-of-ten notation, conversion factors between different units, the Greek alphabet, and useful data for the solar system. To solve some problems you will need to refer to the appendix to get numerical data.

We hope that the material in this manual will complement the conceptual ideas that you will learn in the textbook. The combination of the two views will give you a more complete understanding of physicists' view of the world around us.

Larry D. Kirkpatrick
Gerald F. Wheeler
Montana State University
November 1991

PHYSICS: A Numerical World View

Table of Contents

Contents

Contents

Contents

Contents

Contents

INTRODUCTION

0.1 How Many Digits?

When you divide 73 by 13 on your calculator, the display reads 5.6153846. How do you know how many digits to record in your answer? In mathematics, there may be no reason to worry about it. In science, however, the numbers, 73 and 13, and the answer represent physical quantities. If we keep too many digits in the answer, we imply a greater precision in the calculated quantity than in the measured quantities. The digits that reflect the precision of the measurements are call *significant digits*.

Although there is a set of rules that would tell you how many to keep in the general case, we will not need to learn these rules. We will simply agree to keep no more than three significant digits in our answers. Therefore,

$$\frac{73}{13} = 5.62$$

In effect we are assuming that the given data have three significant digits even if they are not written out explicitly. In this case, we are assuming that 73.0/13.0 = 5.62. In this same spirit, we will usually not keep trailing zeros after the decimal point in our answers.

When keeping the three significant digits, we will round our answer before dropping the extra digits. To do this, look at the fourth digit. If it is less than 5, drop the remaining digits. If it is 5 or greater, add 1 to the third digit and then drop it and the remaining digits. The following examples illustrate this procedure:

Example 0.1.1

Round the numbers 12.34321 and 2.3456789 to three significant digits.

Look at the fourth-digit in the first number. Since this 4 is less than 5, we simply drop it and the remaining digits.

$$12.34321 \rightarrow 12.3$$

In the second number, the fourth digit is a 5. Therefore, we add one to the third digit before dropping the remaining digits.

$$2.3456789 \rightarrow 2.35$$

Practice[1]

Round the following numbers to three significant digits: a) 6.783; b) 9.846; c) 34.89; and d) 56.34.

---

[1] 6.78; 9.85; 34.9; and 56.3

If the number is smaller than 1, we ignore the leading zeros in counting significant digits as their only purpose is to locate the decimal point. Therefore, 0.013 has only two significant digits. Similarly, if the number is larger than 1000, such as 15,325, we replace the "dropped" digits with zeros to keep the decimal in its proper place. Therefore, we would round this number to read 15,300.

Example 0.1.2

Round the following numbers to three significant digits: 0.003412 and 19,651.

In the first number, we look for the first non-zero digit and count over three more digits. Since this 2 is less than 5, we drop it and all following digits.

$$0.003412 \rightarrow 0.00341$$

In the second number we add one to the third digit since the fourth digit is a 5. Then we convert all of the digits beyond the 7 to zeros.

$$19,651 \rightarrow 19,700$$

Practice[2]

Round the following to three significant digits: a) 0.028632; b) 31,557,082.

◆ ◆ ◆

You may keep additional digits in your calculator during computations and round off the answer at the end. If you are doing the calculations by hand, you can save yourself work by rounding off intermediate results to 4 digits. The small differences in the answers are not important.

In the text, we rounded the value of the acceleration due to gravity from 9.81 m/s/s to 10 m/s/s to make calculations easier. In this manual, we will use three significant digits as we do with most other numbers.

There are occasions where we will use more than three significant digits. This usually happens when an effect is hidden when only three signifigant digits are used. As an example, in Chapter 25 we calculate the mass difference between a nucleus and its constituent protons and neutrons. The mass difference typically occurs in the third significant digit and would not be very accurate unless we use additional digits.

---

[2] 0.0286; 31,600,000

0.2 Units

It is tempting to ignore the units associated with numerical values, but this can be the source of a lot of trouble. For instance, if you ask for a board with a length of 8, it is not clear if you want a board that is 8 inches, 8 feet, or 8 yards long. Obviously, you will be upset if you ordered an 8-ft stud and got an 8-in. stick. In communicating your numerical results, it is very important to state your units.

You have probably been told many times that you cannot add apples and oranges. This is a reminder that when you add or subtract numbers, they must have the same units. You obviously cannot add a length to a time, but you must also be careful when adding lengths. You must make sure that all of your length measurements are in the same units.

It is a very good habit to include the units for all numbers used in calculations. These units produce the units in the answer and help avoid a variety of problems. For instance, the units are a check that we have used a consistent procedure. If we incorrectly calculate a speed and get a number with units of length x time, we know that we have made an error since speed has units of length/time. Units are also a check that we have used a consistent set of measurements. We should not use the speed of a car in miles per hour in an equation that is expecting all speeds to be given in meters per second. Our answer will not make any sense.

The units can also serve as a check to be sure that we do not leave out one of the measurements in a calculation. We should always manipulate the units using the rules of algebra to see if they give the expected units for the answer.

Example 0.2.1

How far does a car travel if it has a constant speed of 80 km/h for 2.5 h?

$$d = vt = \left(80 \, \frac{km}{h}\right)(2.5 \, h)$$

Canceling the two h's, we see that our answer is 200 km. Therefore, we would be very wrong to give our answer as 200 m. If we had incorrectly divided the speed by the time, we would have obtained 32 km/h^2, something that is only seen as nonsense when we examine the units.

Practice[3]

How far does an airplane travel in 3.2 h at a constant speed of 800 km/h?

◆ ◆ ◆

---

[3] 2560 km

0.3 Changing Units

There are often times when we need to convert a measurement in one set of units into another set of units. This won't cause any confusion about whether we should multiply or divide by the conversion factor if we follow a definite procedure each time.

The procedure uses multiplication by 1. This works because 1 is the only number that does not change the value of the measurement. However, it can change the *form* of the number. The technique involves writing 1 as a fraction with its numerator equal to its denominator. For instance, we have learned that 1 foot is the same as 12 inches. Thus,

$$\frac{12\ in.}{1\ ft} = 1$$

We can now convert measurements in feet to the equivalent values in inches by multiplying by 1 in this form. How do you know whether to multiply by $\left(\dfrac{12\ in.}{1\ ft}\right)$ or by $\left(\dfrac{1\ ft}{12\ in.}\right)$? Always choose the fraction so that you cancel out the old unit. This will automatically put the new unit in its proper place.

Example 0.3.1

How many inches are there in 8 ft?

$$8\ ft \left(\frac{12\ in.}{1\ ft}\right) = 96\ in.$$

Practice[4]

How many feet are there in 100 in?

◆   ◆   ◆

You can do the conversions in several steps such as converting miles to feet and then feet to inches by multiplying by both forms of 1. You can also convert two units at the same time.

Example 0.3.2

What is a speed of 60 mph expressed in ft/s?

---

[4] 8.33 ft

$$60 \ \frac{miles}{h} \left(\frac{5280 \, ft}{1 \, mile} \right) \left(\frac{1 \, h}{60 \, min} \right) \left(\frac{1 \, min}{60 \, s} \right) = 88 \ \frac{ft}{s}$$

Practice[5]

How many inches are there in 100 yards?

◆   ◆   ◆

A list of conversion factors is given in the Appendix at the back of this manual that can be used to make the "1" fractions.

Problems

1. Round the following numbers to 3 significant digits: a) 3.14159; b) 23,692; c) 0.55551; d) 0.0098372.
2. Round the following numbers to 3 significant digits: a) 0.003421; b) 0.4567; c) 2.1817; d) 345,333.
3. Round the following answers to 3 significant digits: a) 51/8; b) 89 x 564.
4. Round the following answers to 3 significant digits: a) 365/478; b) 2.57 x 0.86.
5. Round the following answers to 3 significant digits:
   a) $(1.26 \times 10^6)/(5.8 \times 10^3)$;
   b) $(1.47 \times 10^9)(3.68 \times 10^5)$.
6. Round the following answers to 3 significant digits:
   a) $(6.35 \times 10^4)/(2.2 \times 10^2)$;
   b) $(7.42 \times 10^2)(1.16 \times 10^3)$.
7. How many inches are there in 1 mile?
8. If there are 16 oz in 1 lb, how many ounces are there in one ton (2000 lb)?
9. Given that there are 2.54 cm in 1 in., how many centimeters are there in 1 ft?
10. Given that 2.54 cm = 1 in., how tall is a 6-ft person in centimeters?
11. How many millimeters are there in 24 km?
12. How many seconds are there in a year?
13. Given that 1 mile = 1.61 km, what is a speed of 65 mph expressed in km/h?
14. Given that 1 mile = 1.61 km, what is speed of 100 km/h expressed in mph?
15. A car has a speed of 30 m/s. What is this speed expressed in km/h?
16. What is a speed limit of 100 km/h expressed in m/s?
*17. How many square centimeters are there in an area of 1 m^2?
*18. How many cubic centimeters are there in a box with a volume of 1 m^3?

---

[5] 3600 in.

1 DESCRIBING MOTION

1.1 Computing Average Speed

The definition of average speed $\bar{s}$ is the distance traveled d divided by the time taken t.

$$\bar{s} = \frac{d}{t}$$

This expression can be used to obtain the average speed whenever we know the total distance traveled and the time required to do this.

Example 1.1.1

A family drove across the United States in a week. If they covered 4800 km, what was their average speed?

Our answer will depend on the unit of time we choose to use. Since we could use weeks, days, or hours, we could have

$$\bar{s} = \frac{4800\ km}{1\ week} = 4800\ km/week$$

$$\bar{s} = \frac{4800\ km}{7\ days} = 686\ km/day$$

$$\bar{s} = \frac{4800\ km}{7 \times 24\ h} = 28.6\ km/h$$

Notice that these values include time for sleeping, eating, and rest stops.

Practice[1]

If they drove 8 h each day, what was the average speed during driving hours? ♦♦

Example 1.1.2

How far can you travel at an average speed of 85 km/h for 4.2 h?

We can algebraically manipulate our definition for average speed to get an expression for the distance traveled by an object traveling at this average speed for the given time.

---

[1] 85.7 km/h

Begin by multiplying both sides of our definition by the time t and then canceling the t's on the right-hand side.

$$\bar{s}\,t = \frac{d}{\cancel{t}}\cancel{t}$$

Switching the two sides of the equation, we obtain our expression.

$$d = \bar{s}\,t$$

Now plug in our given values to get our answer.

$$d = \bar{s}\,t = \left(85\,\frac{km}{h}\right)(4.2\,h) = 357\,km$$

Practice[2]

How far can an airplane fly in 3.5 h at 180 km/h?

Example 1.1.3

How long would it require to travel 730 km at an average speed of 80 km/h?

We can obtain the expression for the time required to travel a given distance at a given average speed by once again manipulating the definition for average speed. We begin by multiplying both sides by the time t as we did in the previous example. We then divide both sides by $\bar{s}$ and cancel the $\bar{s}$'s on the left-hand side.

$$\bar{s}\,t = d$$

$$\frac{\cancel{\bar{s}}\,t}{\cancel{\bar{s}}} = \frac{d}{\bar{s}}$$

We can now plug in our numbers to obtain our answer.

$$t = \frac{d}{\bar{s}} = \frac{730\,km}{80\,km/h} = 9.13\,h$$

Note that dividing by the units km/h is equivalent to multiplying by h/km. We can then cancel the km's to get hours as the unit for our answer.

---

[2] 630 km

Practice[3]

How long would it take a Cessna 172 to fly a distance of 500 km at an average speed of 175 km/h?

♦ ♦ ♦

1.2 Images of Speed

Another way of representing motion was discovered when a French mathematician invented the technique of graphing. Although there are a number of types of graphs, we will focus on the common two-axis graph that represents the relationship between two quantities. These graphs display relationships between a variety of quantities such as the rise and fall of the Dow Jones Industrial Average with time, your weight on each day of the year, or the distances it takes to stop a car traveling at different speeds.

We will use graphs to represent the motion of the puck shown in Fig. 1-5 in the text and show how this representation is especially valuable for analyzing motion. The horizontal axis will represent time. For convenience, imagine that we start a stopwatch at the beginning of the motion. Therefore, the time axis usually starts with zero and advances into the future. The vertical axis represents the position of the object. Since time and position are totally separate quantities, there is no relationship between the two scales; we are free to choose each one independently to best represent the situation. The choices for our example come from examining the data in Table 1-1 in the text. Because the puck traveled between 2 cm and 82 cm, a good choice for the vertical axis is a scale ranging from 0 to 90 cm with divisions every 10 cm. The strobe images occurred every 1/10 second. Since there are 6 images, the scale for the time axis is chosen to range from 0 to 0.6 s with divisions each 0.1 s.

The graph in Fig. 1.2.1 was drawn using these choices. Each data point on the graph represents a particular space-time event. The extreme, upper right-hand point, for example, tells us that the puck was at a position 82 cm from the spot we called "zero" at 0.6 s.

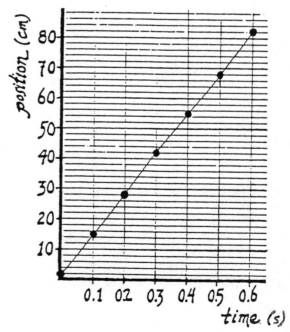

Fig. 1.2.1

---

[3] 2.86 h

1 Describing Motion

This position-time graph is more than a picture; we can obtain information about the speed of the puck by looking at the steepness of the straight lines connecting the data points. Since the time intervals are all the same, the fastest speed occurs when the puck covers the most distance in one of these time intervals. On the graph this happens when the vertical separation of two adjacent data points is the greatest. This causes the line connecting the two points to be the steepest. The steepest lines occur between 0.2 s and 0.3 s and between 0.5 s and 0.6 s. Notice that this agrees with the calculations in Table 1-1 in the text, where we discovered that the average speed during these time intervals was 140 cm/s.

We measure the steepness of a line by taking the ratio of the *rise* over the *run*, a quantity known as the **slope**.

$$slope = \frac{rise}{run}$$

The rise of the line is the difference between the two vertical values, while the run is the difference between the two corresponding horizontal values. The slopes of the straight line segments in Fig. 1.2.1 represent the average speeds during each interval.

We can now use this concept to look at the average speed for the entire trip. In Fig. 1.2.2 we have redrawn the graph and replaced the dot-to-dot lines with a single straight line. This is often done in graphing when additional information suggests it. In this case, it is reasonable to believe that the motion was not jerky, but smooth. We believe that the jerkiness in the data was due to uncertainties in measuring the positions of the puck and <u>not</u> in the motion of the puck itself. Although there are mathematical techniques for determining this line, we use the "eyeball" method. Assuming that the measurements were too big as often as they were too small, the best straight line should have about half the data points above the line and half below the line as shown in Fig. 1.2.2. It just happens for this graph that the best straight line passes through the first and last data points. This is not a requirement. In choosing the best line, it is possible to miss any given point, or even all the points.

We can now use any two points <u>on the straight line</u> to calculate the slope of the line

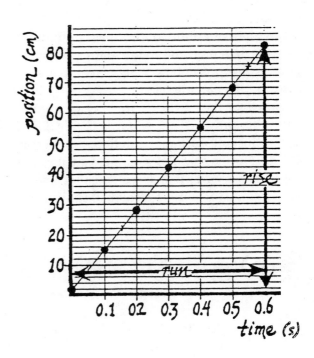

Fig. 1.2.2

and obtain the average speed for the motion. It is more accurate to use widely separated points as this reduces the effects of uncertainties in reading the values from the graph. Because the straight line passes through the end points, we could use them to calculate our slope. However, let's choose the points at 0.15 s and 0.55 s. Then we have

$$rise = 75\,cm - 22\,cm = 53\,cm$$

$$run = 0.55\,s - 0.15\,s = 0.4\,s$$

$$average\ speed = slope = \frac{rise}{run} = \frac{53\,cm}{0.4\,s} = 133\,cm/s$$

Question[4]

What would the graph look like if the puck were moving faster?

1.3 Instantaneous Speed

While the concept of an instantaneous speed is easy to comprehend, calculating it is another matter. The problem lies in the fact that dividing by an "instant of time" leads to mathematical confusion because dividing by zero is not defined in ordinary arithmetic. Isaac Newton invented the mathematics of calculus to deal with such problems. Fortunately, our graphical representation gives us an easy way of obtaining the instantaneous speed without resorting to calculus.

Consider the "strobe" drawing of a puck moving from left to right in Fig. 1.3.1. The data from this drawing are given in Table 1.3.1. To determine the instantaneous speed of the puck at any instant during its motion, we start by making the position-time graph shown in Fig. 1.3.2. Notice that the steepness of the line changes during the motion, indicating that the speed is varying; if it were constant, the curve would be a straight line. Portions of the curve are straight (or almost straight), indicating that parts of the trip had constant speeds. For

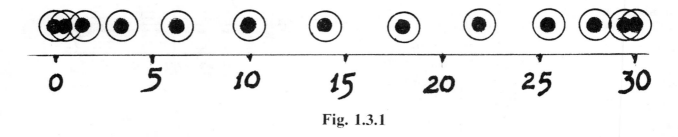

Fig. 1.3.1

---

[4] A puck with a faster speed would need to cover more distance in the same time. Therefore, the straight line would have a steeper slope.

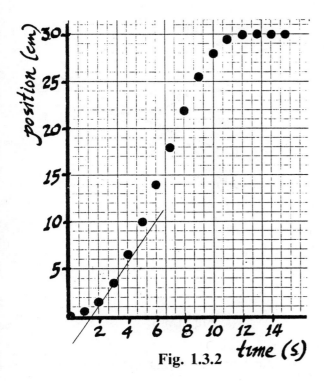

Fig. 1.3.2

Table 1.3.1

Time (s)	Position (cm)	Av. Speed (cm/s)
0	0.0	
		0.5
1	0.5	
		1.0
2	1.5	
		2.0
3	3.5	
		3.0
4	6.5	
		3.5
5	10.0	
		4.0
6	14.0	
		4.0
7	18.0	
		4.0
8	22.0	
		3.5
9	25.5	
		2.5
10	28.0	
		1.5
11	29.5	
		0.5
12	30.0	
		0.0
13	30.0	
		0.0
14	30.0	
		0.0
15	30.0	

instance, look at the end of the motion. The curve is straight and horizontal. The rise is zero, showing that the speed is zero. This can be verified by examining the last four entries in Table 1.3.1; the position of the puck doesn't change.

The curve is almost horizontal at the beginning, indicating that the motion started out with a low speed. As the motion proceeds, the curve becomes steeper, indicating an increasing speed. It reaches its maximum speed between 5 s and 8 s, and then it slows down and stops.

Question[5]

What do you suppose a vertical line on this graph would represent?

---

[5] Unlike the horizontal line, a vertical line does not represent a real motion because the object would have to be in many different positions at the same time, a physical impossibility. You could also think of it as representing an infinite speed, another impossibility.

How do we calculate the speed for a time when the curve is not straight? We can calculate the slope of the line tangent to the curve at that time. When the curve is rather smooth, the tangent is a line that touches the curve at only one point. You can imagine taking two points that are equal distances on each side of the point of interest and connecting them with an extended line as shown in Fig. 1.3.3. Now imagine moving the two points along the curve at the same speed while carrying the line along with them. As the points approach each other, the line becomes the tangent line as shown. In the case of a circular arc, the tangent line is perpendicular to the radius.

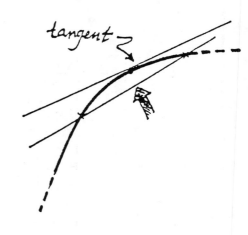

Fig. 1.3.3

Example 1.3.1

A tangent line has been drawn in Fig. 1.3.2 for the time of 3 s. What is the slope of this line?

Let's choose the positions corresponding to t = 2 s and t = 6 s.

$$slope \ = \ \frac{rise}{run} \ = \ \frac{10 \, cm - 1 \, cm}{6 \, s - 2 \, s} \ = \ \frac{9 \, cm}{4 \, s} \ = \ 2.3 \, cm/s$$

Therefore the instantaneous speed at 3 s is about 2.3 cm/s.

Practice[6]

Determine the instantaneous speed at 9 s.

◆   ◆   ◆

1.4 Velocity-Time Graphs

Just as it was useful to draw the position-time graph to get a feeling for the speed of the object, it is useful to draw a velocity-time graph to develop a feeling for the acceleration. From the similarities of the definitions of average velocity and average acceleration, we know

---

[6] You should have obtained something close to 3 cm/s.

that the slope of the curve on the velocity-time graph gives us the magnitude of the acceleration. Since we have already calculated the average speeds for our motion in Table 1.3.1, let's use these values as approximations to the instantaneous speeds. Because we don't know when in the time intervals the average speeds actually occurred, a reasonable guess is to plot them in Fig. 1.4.1 at the middle of each interval.

We see that the acceleration at the beginning was not zero because the tangent to the curve is not horizontal. During the first few seconds, not only was the speed increasing, the acceleration was also increasing as indicated by the increased steepness of the velocity-time curve. From 3 s to 7 s, the acceleration was getting smaller, but the speed was still increasing. After 7 s the acceleration was reversed and the speed decreased, eventually causing the puck to stop at about 13 s.

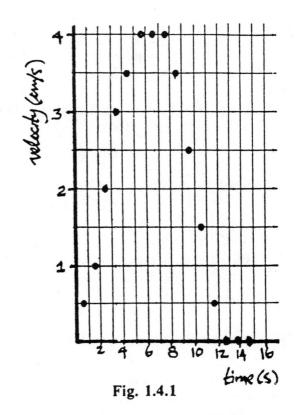

Fig. 1.4.1

Questions[7] Where did the acceleration have the maximum value in the forward direction? In the backward direction? Where was the acceleration equal to zero?

1.5 Speed with Direction

Velocity is a vector quantity that includes direction as well as speed. In the case of motion along a straight line, we can describe the direction with a plus or a minus sign. Assume that we measure distances from west to east as is done by the mile markers along Interstate highways. We then say that something moving east has a positive velocity and that something moving west has a negative velocity. We can then calculate the change in velocity by taking the difference of the final and initial velocities <u>including their signs</u>.

---

[7] The steepest part of the rising curve occurs at about 2.5 s. Therefore, the maximum acceleration in the forward direction occurs at this time. The maximum value for the backward direction occurs between 9 and 11 s. For the acceleration to be zero, the slope of the tangent line must be zero. This occurs at the top of the curve near 7 s.

Example 1.5.1

What is the change in velocity that occurs when a car traveling at 25 m/s east turns around and travels 25 m/s west?

Being careful to assign a plus sign to the eastward velocity, and to assign a minus sign to the westward velocity, we have

$$\Delta v = v_f - v_i = (25 \, m/s) - (-25 \, m/s) = 50 \, m/s$$

Since the answer is positive, the change in velocity points toward the east.
We will study velocities that do not lie along a straight line in Chapter 3.

Practice[8]

What is the change in velocity if the directions are reversed?

◆ ◆ ◆

1.6 Computing Acceleration

In the text, we calculated the acceleration of a car that increased its speed from 40 mph to 60 mph in a time of 20 s.

$$\bar{a} = \frac{\Delta v}{t} = \frac{v_f - v_i}{t} = \frac{60 \, mph - 40 \, mph}{20 \, s} = \frac{20 \, mph}{20 \, s} = 1 \, mph/s$$

The car can also have a decrease in its speed. Suppose that the car slowed down from 60 mph to 40 mph in the same 20 s. (Notice that this reverses the initial and final velocities.) We calculate the change in velocity in the same way by subtracting the initial velocity from the final velocity. Therefore, the car's average acceleration would be

$$\bar{a} = \frac{\Delta v}{t} = \frac{v_f - v_i}{t} = \frac{40 \, mph - 60 \, mph}{20 \, s} = \frac{-20 \, mph}{20 \, s} = -1 \, mph/s$$

The value of the acceleration is the same as it was in our first example, except for the minus sign. At first glance it is tempting to say that the negative value shows up in the calculation because the object is slowing down. Although this is true in this case, the negative value really results from our choosing the direction of travel as the "positive" direction.

---

[8] -50 m/s where the minus sign means that the change in velocity points westward.

1 Describing Motion

Remembering that velocity is a vector quantity that includes the direction as well as the speed, we can describe the direction with a plus or a minus sign. Assume that we say that something traveling east has a positive velocity, while something traveling west has a negative velocity. We must then include the signs in the calculation to take care of these directions.

Example 1.6.1

What is the change in velocity of a car traveling westward that speeds up from 40 mph to 60 mph?

Adopting east as the positive direction, we have

$$\Delta v = v_f - v_i = -60\, mph - (-40\, mph) = -20\, mph$$

This means that the car is traveling 20 mph faster in the negative direction, that is, westward. Note that this car would have an average acceleration of -1 mph/s if this change took place in 20 s.

Practice[9]

What would the average acceleration be if the car were traveling eastward?

◆ ◆ ◆

Mathematically, the direction of the acceleration arises from the vector nature of velocity. When we take the difference of two vectors, the answer is also a vector. Because acceleration is the difference of two velocity vectors divided by the time interval, it is a vector quantity, and thus has a direction. As with velocity, the direction of the acceleration along a straight line is given by a plus or minus sign. The average acceleration in the last example is negative, indicating that the acceleration points westward.

But how do we know from the sign of the acceleration whether the car is speeding up or slowing down? In the text, the car was moving in the positive direction and speeding up. When we calculated the acceleration, we obtained a positive value. Therefore, the acceleration was in the same direction as the velocity. In our last example, the car was traveling in the negative direction and speeding up, and we obtained a negative acceleration. This leads us to the conclusion that when the velocity and acceleration vectors point in the same direction, the car speeds up. Conversely, when they point in opposite directions, the car slows down in agreement with our earlier calculation.

---

[9] 1 mph/s

Example 1.6.2

Suppose that a ball is traveling at 10 m/s in a direction that we decide to call positive and that 6 s later it is moving in the opposite direction at 20 m/s. What is the average acceleration of the ball?

$$\overline{a} = \frac{\Delta v}{t} = \frac{v_f - v_i}{t} = \frac{-20\,m/s - 10\,m/s}{6\,s} = \frac{-30\,m/s}{6\,s} = -5\,m/s^2$$

Once again the minus sign tells us that the direction of the acceleration is in the negative direction. Since this is opposite to the initial velocity of the ball, the ball slows down. After the ball's speed is reduced to zero, the negative acceleration causes the ball to speed up in the negative direction.

It is standard to write the units of acceleration as m/s^2 rather than m/s/s, which is a bit ambiguous as to the order of division. We can see that these forms are the same as follows

$$m/s/s \equiv \frac{m/s}{s} = \frac{m}{s}\frac{1}{s} = \frac{m}{s^2}$$

Practice[10]

What is the average acceleration of a car that changes its velocity of -20 m/s to a velocity of 20 m/s in 10 s?

◆ ◆ ◆

1.7 Free Fall: Making a Rule of Nature

Using our knowledge of how a ball behaves when dropped, we can fill in a table showing its acceleration, its speed, and the distance it has fallen at the end of each second until it strikes the ground. We know that the acceleration has a constant value throughout the fall. This causes the ball to speed up by 9.81 m/s each second. We can also calculate how far it has fallen using the equation

$$d = \frac{1}{2}at^2$$

---

[10] 4 m/s^2

time (s)	acceleration (m/s/s)	speed (m/s)	distance (m)	Δdistance (m)
0	9.81	0	0	
1	9.81	9.81	4.91	4.91
2	9.81	19.6	19.6	14.7
3	9.81	29.4	44.1	24.5

Notice that the change in distance tabulated in the last column behaves in a regular way. After the first entry, the distance fallen during each succeeding second increases by 9.81 m. This distance can be calculated directly. For any object, the distance traveled during a time interval is just the average speed during that time multiplied by the length of the time interval. For objects with a constant acceleration, the average speed is the average of the initial and final speeds.

$$\overline{s} = \frac{s_f + s_i}{2}$$

Example 1.7.1

How far will the ball fall between $t = 3$ s and $t = 4$ s?

$$\Delta d = \overline{s}t = \frac{s_i + s_f}{2}t = \frac{(29.4 \, m/s) + (39.2 \, m/s)}{2}(1 \, s) = 34.3 \, m$$

Practice[11]

How far will the ball fall between $t = 3$ s and $t = 5$ s?

◆ ◆ ◆

1.8 Starting with an Initial Velocity

Up until this point we have not had a relationship that allows us to calculate what happens if a falling object is initially in motion. We can use our definition of average acceleration to

---

[11] 78.5 m

determine what happens to the velocity. By writing out Δv explicitly as the difference between the initial and final velocities, we have

$$a = \frac{v_f - v_i}{t}$$

where we have not use $\bar{a}$ because the instantaneous acceleration is constant and equal to the average acceleration. Rearranging terms yields

$$v_f = v_i + at$$

This form of the relationship tells us that the acceleration causes a fixed change in the velocity, and it doesn't matter if the initial velocity is zero or not.

Example 1.8.1

In the text we discussed a ball thrown into the air with an initial upward velocity of 19.6 m/s. What's the velocity of the ball after 4 s?

Choosing the upward direction to be positive, we have

$$v_f = v_i + at = 19.6\,m/s + (-9.81\,m/s^2)(4\,s) = -19.6\,m/s$$

We used a negative value for the acceleration due to gravity since it points downward. Notice that this answer - that the ball is falling at 19.6 m/s downward - agrees with the verbal argument given in the text.

Practice[12]

What is the velocity of the ball at 2 s?

◆ ◆ ◆

The formula for the change in position when there's an initial velocity is a bit more complicated and we give it here without a derivation.

$$d = v_i t + \frac{1}{2}at^2$$

The first term on the right-hand side of the equation tells us how far the object would have

---

[12] Zero. Therefore, we reason that the ball is at the top of its path.

gone without any acceleration, while the second term yields the distance for the special case of no initial velocity. The sum of the two distances gives us the total change in position.

Example 1.8.2

Returning to our example, what is the change in position for the thrown ball after 2 s?

$$d = v_i t + \frac{1}{2}at^2$$

$$= (19.6 \, m/s)(2 \, s) + \frac{1}{2}(-9.81 \, m/s^2)(2 \, s)^2$$

$$= 39.2 \, m - 19.6 \, m = 19.6 \, m$$

Again, each term in the equation represents different contributions to the ball's upward motion. The first term tells us the ball would have gone up 39.2 m without any gravity, but the effect of the acceleration due to gravity, expressed in the second term, reduced this by 19.6 m. The net result is that the ball rises 19.6 m in the first 2 s.

Example 1.8.3

What is the change in position after 4 s?

$$d = v_i t + \frac{1}{2}at^2$$

$$= (19.6 \, m/s)(4 \, s) + \frac{1}{2}(-9.81 \, m/s^2)(4 \, s)^2$$

$$= 78.4 \, m - 78.4 \, m = 0$$

At first glance this answer might seem a bit surprising since the ball has obviously traveled some distance. The key to understanding this result is realizing that *d* is the change in the position of the ball. Since the ball returned to the same position as it started, its change in position is zero. To get the total distance traveled, add the 19.6 m for the upward path to the 19.6 m for the downward path to get a total of 39.2 m.

Practice[13]

Where is the ball at 3 s?

◆ ◆ ◆

---

[13] 14.7 m above the beginning height.

Problems

1. What is the average speed of a jet transport that flies 5000 km in 6 h 20 min?

2. What is the average speed of a cruise ship that covers 350 km in 24 h?

3. An experienced hiker can comfortably walk 10.5 miles in 3 h. What is the hiker's average speed?

4. If a cheetah runs 1.5 miles in 2 min, what is its average speed in mph?

5. In 1954 Roger Bannister was the first person to run a mile in less than 4 min. His time was 3 min 59.4 s. What was his average speed in mph?

6. In 1991 Carl Lewis broke the record for the 100-m dash in a time of 9.86 s? What was his average speed in mph?

7. Suppose that you begin a trip from the middle of a large city. During the first hour you manage to average 30 km/h. Then you hit the open road and average 60 km/h for the next 2 h. What is your average speed for the trip? (*Hint:* The average speed is not the average of the two speeds.)

8. While driving across the deserts of Nevada, you maintain an average speed of 105 km/h for 2.8 h. You then turn onto a secondary road for 3.2 h, where you maintain an average speed of 60 km/h. What is your average speed for the entire trip?

9. If the earth has an average orbital speed of 107,000 km/h, how far does it travel in one year?

10. If you can drive across Montana along Interstate 90 in 15 h at an average speed of 75 km/h, how far is it across Montana?

11. It is 4470 km between New York City and Los Angeles. If a cyclist can ride for 8 h/day at an average speed of 30 km/h, how many days would it take to make the ride?

12. Assuming that a space ship traveling to Mars has to travel 300 million km at an average speed of 20,000 km/h, how many months would it take to make the journey?

13. Fig. 1.P.1 is a position-time graph for the motion of a model rocket. What is the instantaneous speed of the rocket 3 s after launch?

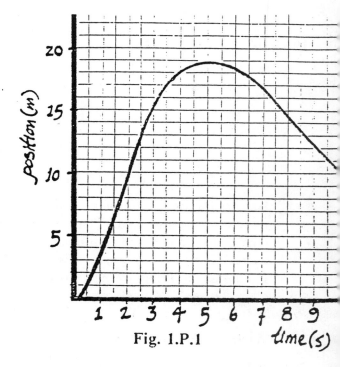

Fig. 1.P.1

14. Fig. 1.P.1 is a position-time graph for the motion of a model rocket. What is the instantaneous speed of the rocket 8 s after launch?

15. A velocity-time graph for a ball falling in air is shown in Fig. 1.P.2. What is the acceleration of the ball 6 s after it is dropped?

16. A velocity-time graph for a ball falling in air is shown in Fig. 1.P.2. What is the acceleration of the ball 14 s after it is dropped?

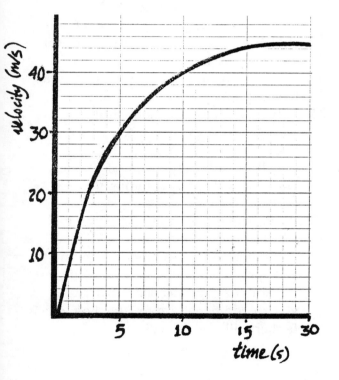

Fig. 1.P.2

17. What is the average acceleration of a car if it speeds up from 50 mph to 65 mph in 3 min?

18. A cheetah can obtain a speed of 72 km/h from a standing start in just 2 s. What is its average acceleration?

19. A Ford Escort can cover 1/4 mile from a standing start in 19.4 s and be going 69 mph at the finish.
    a. What is its average acceleration?
    b. What is its average speed?

20. In 1975 Don Garlits set the world's record for AA fuel dragsters by traveling 1/4 mile in 5.9 s from a standing start. He was traveling 254 mph at the end of the quarter mile.
    a. What was his average acceleration?
    b. What was his average speed?

21. What is the average acceleration of a car that is initially traveling at 100 km/h north, but is traveling 80 km/h south 1 minute later?

22. An airplane was flying north at 180 km/h. Ten minutes later it is flying south at the same speed. What was its average acceleration?

23. A baseball traveling at 90 mph is hit back at the pitcher with a speed of 110 mph. If the ball remains in contact with the bat for 0.01 s, what is the average acceleration of the ball?

24. A bug near the outer edge of a long-play phonograph record is traveling with a speed of 50 cm/s. If it takes the bug 0.9 s to go half way around so that it is going in the opposite direction, what average acceleration must it have during this time?

25. A ball falling at 20 m/s bounces on the floor and has a speed of 16 m/s upward when it returns to the same height. If this requires 6 s, what is the average acceleration of the ball?

26. What is the average acceleration of a ball that is thrown vertically upward on the moon with a speed of 2 m/s if it takes 2.5 s to return?

27. A ball is dropped from the top of a building that is 78.5 m tall. Neglecting the effects of air resistance, construct a table showing the speed of the ball and the distance the ball has fallen at the end of each second until the ball strikes the ground.

28. Construct a table for the speed of a rock and the distance it has fallen at each second if is dropped from the top of a 123-m cliff.

29. A ball is thrown vertically upward with an initial speed of 29.4 m/s. Neglecting the effects of air resistance, construct a table showing the speed of the ball and the distance the ball has risen at the end of each second until the ball reaches the top of its path.

30. Construct a table for the speed of a ball and its position above the ground at the end of each second if it is thrown upward at 39.3 m/s.

31. A ball is thrown vertically upward with an initial speed of 29.4 m/s.
    a. What is the value of the instantaneous speed when the ball reaches its maximum height?
    b. How long does it take to reach this height?
    c. How long does it take the ball to fall from the maximum height to the ground? (*Hint*: Remember that the upward motion is symmetric to the downward motion.)
    d. What is the maximum height reached by the ball?
    e. How fast is the ball going when it strikes the ground?

32. A ball is thrown vertically upward with an initial speed of 39.3 m/s.
    a. How long does it take the ball to reach the top of its path?
    b. What is the maximum height reached by the ball?

33. A truck is traveling along a straight stretch of freeway at 20 m/s. How far will it travel in 10 s? If it accelerates at 1 m/s^2 to pass another truck, how far will it travel in the next 10 s?

34. A car is traveling along a straight stretch of freeway at 30 m/s. How far will it travel in 10 s? If it accelerates at 1 m/s^2 to slow down for a speed trap, how far will it travel in the next 10 s?

35. A ball falls past a window traveling at 15 m/s. How far will it fall during the next 2 s?

36. A ball is traveling upward at 25 m/s. How far will it travel during the next 2 s?

37. Assume that you are traveling 60 mph when you see a hazard ahead. If it takes you 1 s to recognize the hazard and apply the brakes, how far will you travel during this second? If it takes you an additional 4 s to stop, how much farther will you travel?

2 EXPLAINING MOTION

2.1 The Net Force

If two forces are applied to an object at right angles to each
other, we can apply the Pythagorean theorem to mathematically
determine the resultant force. If we label the lengths of the three
sides of a right triangle as shown in Fig. 2.1.1, the Pythagorean
theorem states that the square of the long side of the triangle is
equal to the sum of the squares of the other two sides.
Symbolically, we have

$$c^2 = a^2 + b^2$$

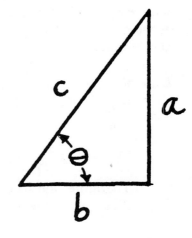

Fig. 2.1.1

The direction of the net force can be measured with a
protractor on a scale drawing. You can also easily obtain the
angle if your calculator has trigonometric functions. Divide the
length of the side opposite the angle θ (in this case a) by the
length of the adjacent side b. Then push the "inv" or "2nd" key
followed by the "tan" key. The answer should appear in the
calculator window.

Example 2.1.1

Assume that two forces are applied to a ball at right angles to each other. One force is
20 newtons to the north and the other is 30 newtons to the west. What is the size of
the resultant force?

We use the Pythagorean theorem to obtain the square of the net force.

$$c^2 = a^2 + b^2 = (20\,N)^2 + (30\,N)^2 = 1300\,N^2$$

We now take the square root to obtain the force.

$$c = \sqrt{1300\,N^2} = 36\,N$$

To obtain the angle, we divide the northward force by the southward force to get 0.667
and punch the keys on the calculator to get $\theta = 33.7°$ north of west.

Practice[1]

What is the net force if the northward force is increased to 40 N?

---

[1] 50 N at an angle of 53.1° north of west

2.2 The Second Law

Newton's second law can be used to find the net force required to accelerate a given mass with a given acceleration. The direction of the net force is the same as the direction of the acceleration. The relationship can also be rearranged algebraically to solve for the acceleration or the mass.

Example 2.2.1

> What net force is required to accelerate a 200-kg box with an acceleration of 4 m/s^2 south?

$$F_{net} = ma = (200\,kg)(4\,m/s^2) = 800\,kg{\cdot}m/s^2 = 800\,N$$

> Therefore, the force must have a size of 800 N and act toward the south, the same direction as the acceleration.

Practice[2]

> What force would be needed to increase the acceleration to 8 m/s^2?

Example 2.2.2

> What acceleration would result from a net force of 200 N acting westward on a person with a mass of 80 kg?

$$a = \frac{F}{m} = \frac{200\,N}{80\,kg} = 2.5\,\frac{N}{kg} \quad 2.5\,\frac{kg{\cdot}m/s^2}{kg} = 2.5\,m/s^2$$

> toward the west.

Practice[3]

> What would the acceleration be if the force were increased to 300 N?

Example 2.2.3

> A crate with an unknown mass undergoes an acceleration of 3.5 m/s^2 when a net force of 1900 N is applied to it. What is the mass of the crate?

---

[2] 1600 N

[3] 3.75 m/s^2 westward

We begin with Newton's second law and divide both sides by the acceleration a to obtain

$$\frac{F_{net}}{a} = \frac{m\,a}{a}$$

$$m = \frac{F_{net}}{a} = \frac{1900\,N}{3.5\,m/s^2} = 543\,\frac{kg \cdot m/s^2}{m/s^2} = 543\,kg$$

Practice[4]

What would the mass be if it required 2300 N to produce the same acceleration?

◆ ◆ ◆

2.3 Computing with the Second Law

Example 2.3.1

A Volkswagen Rabbit with a small driver has a mass of approximately 1000 kg and can accelerate from rest to 22.4 m/s (50 mph) in 7.9 s. What is the net force on the Rabbit? We begin by finding its average acceleration.

$$\bar{a} = \frac{\Delta v}{t} = \frac{v_f - v_i}{t} = \frac{(22.4 - 0)\,m/s}{7.9\,s} = 2.84\,m/s^2$$

This allows us to calculate the average net force exerted on the car.

$$F_{net} = ma = (1000\,kg)(2.84\,m/s^2) = 2840\,N$$

If our driver gets out and four huge football players get into the car, the total mass might climb to 1420 kg. We would then expect the average acceleration to decrease. If we assume that the Rabbit's driving force doesn't change, we can calculate the new acceleration.

$$a = \frac{F_{net}}{m} = \frac{2840\,N}{1420\,kg} = 2\,m/s^2$$

In addition, we can rearrange our definition of acceleration to determine the time it would now take to accelerate from rest to 22.4 m/s.

---

[4] 657 kg

$$t = \frac{\Delta v}{a} = \frac{(22.4 - 0)\,m/s}{2\,m/s^2} = 11.2\,s$$

These calculations can be tested in a real experiment. The point here is that our rules allow us to make statements about the Rabbit's performance before the experiment is done.

Practice[5]

What would the average acceleration be if two 100-kg football players got out?

♦ ♦ ♦

2.4 Weight

Calculating the weight of an object under the influence of the earth's gravitational attraction is an application of Newton's second law. The acceleration due to gravity *g* has a constant downward value near the earth's surface.

Example 2.4.1

What is the weight of a football tackle with a mass of 150 kg?

$$W = mg = (150\,kg)(9.81\,m/s^2) = 1470\,N \quad (337\,lb)$$

Practice[6]

What is the weight of a ballerina with a mass of 46 kg?

Example 2.4.2

What is the mass of a car that has a weight of 15,000 N?

Solving our equation for the mass, we have

$$m = \frac{W}{g} = \frac{15,000\,N}{9.81\,m/s^2} = 1530\,\frac{N}{m/s^2} = 1530\,\frac{kg \cdot m/s^2}{m/s^2} = 1530\,kg$$

---

[5] This reduces the mass to 1220 kg and the average acceleration becomes 2.33 m/s².

[6] 451 N

Practice[7]

What is the mass of a person with a weight of 850 N?

Example 2.4.3

What is the weight of a 80-kg person standing on Mars where the acceleration due to gravity is 3.7 m/s^2?

$$W = mg = (80\,kg)(3.7\,m/s^2) = 296\,N$$

This is compared with a weight of 785 N on earth.

◆   ◆   ◆

2.5 Friction

To a good approximation, the sliding frictional force acting on an object is proportional to the force keeping the object in contact to the surface. This force is called the *normal* force because it acts perpendicular to the surface. For a horizontal surface with no other vertical forces acting, the normal force is the weight of the object. This can be written

$$F = \mu N$$

where μ is the coefficient of sliding friction. The value of μ depends on the types of surfaces but is insensitive to the normal force and the speed of the object.

Example 2.5.1

What is the frictional force that would act on a 50-kg crate if the coefficient of sliding friction is 0.123?

$$F = \mu N = \mu mg = (0.123)(50\,kg)(9.81\,m/s^2) = 60.3\,N$$

Example 2.5.2

Assume that the crate in the previous example has a maximum static friction of 100 N. It requires an applied force in excess of 100 N to get the crate moving at all. If the applied force is 110 N, what will the acceleration of the crate be?

---

[7] 86.6 kg

$$a = \frac{F_{net}}{m} = \frac{(110\,N - 60.3\,N)}{50\,kg} = 1\,m/s^2$$

We used the value of the sliding friction to calculate the net force because that is the frictional force that acts while the crate is moving.

Example 2.5.3

If we observe the crate in the previous example accelerating at 2 m/s^2, what must be the value of the applied force?

The net force is given by Newton's second law.

$$F_{net} = ma = (50\,kg)(2\,m/s^2) = 100\,N$$

However, we must push with a force that overcomes the sliding friction and still yields a net force of 100 N. Therefore, we must push with a force of 160 N.

Practice [8]

What acceleration would a 210-N force produce?

◆ ◆ ◆

Problems

1. What is the net force produced by the following forces; 4 N acting toward the east, 10 N acting toward the southwest, and 7 acting toward the north?

2. Three forces act on a toy boat; 99 N to the north, 99 N to the east, and 40 N to the southwest. What is the net force on the boat?

3. A force of 38 N acts to the right and a force of 54 N acts downward. What force is needed to produce no acceleration?

4. A light suspended from the ceiling has a weight of 120 N and is being pulled sideways with a force of 35 N. What force does the suspending cord exert on the light?

5. What net force is needed to accelerate a car at 3 m/s^2 east if it has a mass of 2400 kg?

6. An airplane has an acceleration of 2 m/s^2 on its take-off roll. If the airplane has a mass of 1050 kg, what is the net force acting on the airplane?

---

[8] The net force of 150 N would give an acceleration of 3 m/s^2.

7. What acceleration is produced by an 882-N force toward the right acting on a 90-kg person?

8. A 90-kg person has a gravitational force of 150 N on the moon. What would the free-fall acceleration on the moon be?

9. If you push a child on roller skates with a force of 63 N and the child accelerates at 1.5 m/s^2, what is the mass of the child?

10. A model train undergoes an acceleration of 0.5 m/s^2 when a net force of 3 N is applied to it. What is the mass of the train?

*11. The same force is applied to two colored objects. The blue one accelerates at 10 m/s^2 and the red one at 40 m/s^2. What is the ratio of their masses? Which one has the smaller mass?

*12. The same force is applied to two toy cars. The milk truck accelerates at 3 m/s^2, while the sports car accelerates at 9 m/s^2. If the sports car has a mass of 0.20 kg, what is the mass of the milk truck?

*13. An ice skater with a mass of 50 kg moves with a constant speed of 10 m/s in a straight line. How long will it take a force of 100 N to stop the skater if it were applied so as to oppose the motion? What would the speed of the skater be if the force were applied for twice as long?

*14. A book sliding along a horizontal table has a constant frictional force of 4 N acting on it. If it has a mass of 1 kg and an initial speed of 8 m/s, how long will it take to come to rest?

15. A tank of air on a distant planet has a mass of 20 kg and a weight of 300 N. What is the value of the acceleration due to gravity on this planet?

16. An astronaut on a moon orbiting a distant planet has a mass of 70 kg and a weight of 140 N. What is the value of the acceleration due to gravity on this moon?

17. A child has a mass of 42 kg and a weight of 412 N when measured on the earth. What weight and mass would the child have if they were determined on the moon where the gravitational force is one-sixth of that on earth?

18. A seismograph is taken to Mars to see if there are any "marsquakes." If it has a mass of 18 kg on earth, what are its mass and weight on Mars. The acceleration due to gravity on Mars is 3.7 m/s^2.

19. A man with a mass of 84 kg is riding in an elevator that is accelerating upward at 0.5 m/s^2. How much force is being exerted on him by the scales?

20. A woman with a mass of 70 kg is riding in an elevator that is accelerating downward at 0.4 m/s^2. How much force is being exerted on her by the scales?

*21. How much lighter does a 128-pound woman feel in an elevator accelerating downward at 1 ft/s^2?

*22. How much heavier does a 192-pound man feel in an elevator accelerating upward at 2 ft/s^2?

23. A box has a mass of 5 kg, a maximum static friction of 8 N, and a sliding friction of 6 N. What is the acceleration of the box with an applied force of 10 N?

24. A person in free fall with a mass of 80 kg experiences a wind resistance of 600 N. What is the acceleration of the person?

25. What is the frictional force acting on a 4.5-kg wagon if it accelerates at 1.2 m/s^2 under an applied force of 8.2 N?

26. A person in free fall has a mass of 66 kg and an acceleration of 0.8 m/s^2. How large is the air resistance?

3 MOTIONS IN SPACE

3.1 Acceleration Revisited

The acceleration of an object is the vector difference of the final and initial velocities divided by the time taken to make the change. For the general case, we can use the graphical techniques developed in the test to obtain the size and direction of the acceleration. If these two velocities are at right angles to each other, we can apply the Pythagorean theorem developed in Section 2.1 on *The Net Force* to mathematically determine the acceleration.

Example 3.2.1

Assume that a car is moving north at 35 mph and, some time later, is then moving west at the same speed. What is the acceleration of the car if the change takes place in 60 s?

We begin by finding the difference in the two velocities. Since they are at right angles to each other, we use the Pythagorean theorem.

$$c^2 = a^2 + b^2 = (35\,mph)^2 + (35\,mph)^2 = 2450\,mph^2$$

$$c = \sqrt{2450\,mph^2} = 49.5\,mph$$

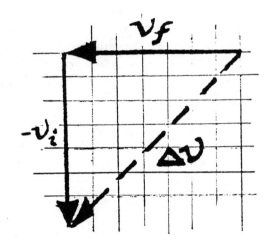

A scale drawing of these velocities like the one in Fig. 3.1.1 shows that the angle of the change in velocity is directly southwest. Or you can use the calculator to find that the angle is 45°. However, you will still need a sketch to determine the general direction.

The value of the acceleration is obtained by dividing this change in velocity by the 60 s it took for the change to occur. Therefore, remembering the vector nature of acceleration, our answer is 0.825 mph/s southwest.

Fig. 3.1.1

Practice[1]

What is the acceleration if the final speed is 20 mph?

♦ ♦ ♦

---

[1] 0.672 mph/s at 29.7° south of west

3.2 Acceleration in Circular Motion

We can determine the size of the centripetal acceleration by examining the force needed to move the ball in a circle. The simple apparatus illustrated in Fig. 3.2.1 gives a way of measuring the force. Select a ball and a weight and tie them to opposite ends of a string that you have threaded through a tube. As you twirl the ball, adjust its motion to keep the hanging weight at a constant height. The hanging weight supplies the centripetal force that is necessary to cause the ball to travel in a circle at a constant speed.

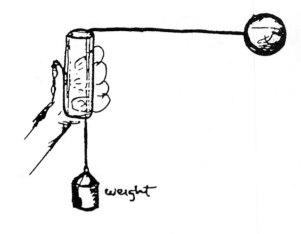

If you now time how long it takes the ball to complete one revolution and measure the radius of the circle to determine its circumference, you can calculate the ball's speed. By doubling the value of the hanging weight you can investigate the dependence of the centripetal force on radius and speed. Return to the same radius as before and

Fig. 3.2.1

obtain the new speed. Then use the original speed and measure the new radius. You can complete your investigation by trying other values of the hanging weight and varying the mass of the ball. After you do all of this, you would find that the magnitude of the centripetal force is given by the mass times the speed squared divided by the radius of the circular path.

$$F = \frac{mv^2}{r} \qquad\qquad \textit{centripetal force}$$

Since the centripetal force is the only force acting on the ball, we can use this expression for the force in Newton's second law.

$$F = \frac{mv^2}{r} = ma$$

Canceling the mass, we obtain an expression for the centripetal acceleration.

$$a = \frac{v^2}{r} \qquad\qquad \textit{centripetal acceleration}$$

Example 3.2.1

A cyclist turns a corner with a radius of 20 m at a speed of 6 m/s. If the mass of the cyclist and cycle is 80 kg, what centripetal force is required?

We begin by calculating the centripetal acceleration.

$$a = \frac{v^2}{r} = \frac{(6\,m/s)^2}{20\,m} = 1.8\,m/s^2$$

We can now insert this value into Newton's second law to get the centripetal force.

$$F_{net} = ma = (80\,kg)(1.8\,m/s^2) = 144\,N$$

Practice[2]

What centripetal force is required if the speed is reduced to 3 m/s?

◆ ◆ ◆

3.3 Projectile Motion

The key idea in solving problems involving projectile motion is to remember that the vertical and horizontal motions are independent of each other. The horizontal motion is very simple because there is no acceleration in the horizontal direction. Therefore, the horizontal component of the velocity v_h is constant and the horizontal distance R traveled is given by

$$R = v_h t$$

where t is the time the ball is in flight.

The vertical motion is just like free fall. Therefore, we can use the two equations for motion with an initial velocity as developed in Section 1.8.

$$v_{vf} = v_{vi} + a_v t$$

$$d = v_{vi} + \frac{1}{2} a_v t^2$$

where d is the change in vertical position, v_{vi} and v_{vf} are the initial and final vertical components of the velocity, respectively, and a_v is the acceleration due to gravity with its sign chosen to agree with the choice of direction in the problem.

Notice that these equations are connected since they both contain the time t. Depending on the problem, we will need to work with one direction to obtain the time, and then use it for the other direction. Typically, we solve for the time using the vertical motion.

---

[2] 36 N

Example 3.3.1

A ball is thrown from an 78.5-m high cliff with a horizontal velocity of 5 m/s. How long is the ball in the air and where does it land on the flat plain below?

To calculate the time t, we look at the vertical motion. We do this by using our formula for the position of the ball.

$$d = v_{vi}t + \frac{1}{2}a_v t^2$$

Let's assume that we call the downward direction positive. Setting $v_{vi} = 0$, $a_v = g$, and $d = H$, we have

$$H = \frac{1}{2}gt^2$$

Solving this equation for t^2, we can substitute in the given values.

$$t^2 = \frac{2H}{g} = \frac{2 \times 78.5\,m}{9.81\,m/s^2} = 16\,s^2$$

Therefore, $t = 4$ s.

We can now use this time to calculate the distance that ball travels horizontally.

$$R = v_h t = (5\,m/s)(4\,s) = 20\,m$$

Practice[3]

How do your answers change if the horizontal speed is increased to 6 m/s?

◆ ◆ ◆

The comparison between Narang and earth can be seen mathematically in the expression for the vertical position of the dart.

$$y = v_{vi}t - \frac{1}{2}gt^2$$

The first term on the right-hand side gives the height of the dart if there were no acceleration like the conditions on Narang. The vertical component of the velocity v_{vi} is constant and the dart climbs by the same amount each second, that is, the dart travels along a straight line.

---

[3] Since the vertical and horizontal motions are independent, the time the ball is in the air remains the same. The increased horizontal speed means that the ball will travel farther during this time, $R = 24$ m.

The second term is just the distance any object falls under the influence of gravity if it starts from rest. The combination of the two terms gives the behavior on earth. Therefore, the dart shot at the gorilla falls away from the straight line exactly as the gorilla falls away from the branch, and the dart will hit its target. Notice that this argument does not depend on the value of v_i. This means that the speed of the dart doesn't matter as long as the dart hits the gorilla before the gorilla hits the ground.

3.4 Torque

Example 3.4.1

Where do the two girls shown in Fig. 3-19 in the text need to sit to balance the seesaw?

We can calculate the required location of the heavier child if we know the weights of both children and the location of the smaller child. Suppose that the children weigh 300 N and 400 N and that the lighter child is 2 m from the pivot point. The lighter child produces a torque of

$$\tau = Fr = (300\,N)(2\,m) = 600\,N{\cdot}m$$

The torque created by the heavier child must have the same value for the seesaw to be balanced. Rearranging the torque equation in order to solve for the moment arm yields

$$r = \frac{\tau}{F} = \frac{600\,N{\cdot}m}{400\,N} = 1.5\,m$$

The heavier child should sit 1.5 m from the pivot.

Practice[4]

Where should the heavier child sit, if the lighter child has a weight of only 200 N?

◆ ◆ ◆

3.5 Rotational Inertia

In the text we argued that the rotational inertia of a body depended on the distribution of mass as well as the total mass of the object. The expression for the rotational inertia I of a

---

[4] 1 m from the pivot

point mass m moving in a circle of radius r is

$$I = mr^2$$

Notice that this expression depends on the square of the radius. This means that the mass farthest from the axle contributes the most to the rotational inertia. The rotational inertia of an extended object is found by summing the contributions of all the "particles" that make up its bulk.

Example 3.5.1

What is the rotational inertia of a thin ring of radius a and total mass M rotating about an axle through the center of the ring and perpendicular to the plane of the ring?

We need to sum up the contributions of each little piece of mass. Let's imagine that we break the ring up into small pieces, each with a mass of m. Then our sum becomes

$$I = ma^2 + ma^2 + ma^2 \ldots$$

Factoring out the common factor a^2, we have

$$I = a^2 (m + m + m \ldots)$$

Since the sum in parentheses is just the total mass M of the ring, we find that

$$I = Ma^2$$

If a = 10 cm and M = 1 kg, we find that the rotational inertia is

$$I = Ma^2 = (1\,kg)(0.1\,m)^2 = 0.01\,kg{\cdot}m^2$$

Practice[5]

What is the value for the rotational inertia if the ring has twice the radius and the same mass?

♦ ♦ ♦

Figure 3.5.1 shows expressions for the rotational inertia of some symmetric objects. Notice that in two cases the same object rotates about different axes, and has different rotational inertia. An object can have many different values for rotational inertia but only one for inertial mass.

---

[5] $0.04\ kg{\cdot}m^2$

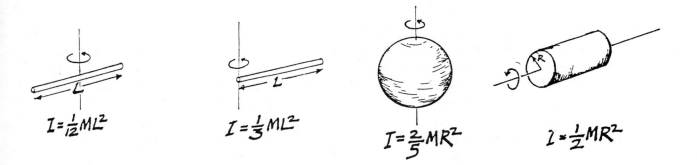

$$I = \tfrac{1}{12}ML^2 \qquad I = \tfrac{1}{3}ML^2 \qquad I = \tfrac{2}{5}MR^2 \qquad I = \tfrac{1}{2}MR^2$$

Fig. 3.5.1

Newton's second law for rotation can be written

$$\tau = I\alpha$$

where τ is the torque, I is the rotational inertia, and α is the rotational acceleration. This particular form of the second law is nice because it is a direct analog of the translational equation. However, it does require that the angles be measured in a special unit known as a radian.

$$1\ radian = \frac{360^o}{2\pi} = 57.3^o$$

Example 3.5.2

What torque would be required to rotate the ring in the previous example with an angular acceleration of 1 rev/min^2?

We first need to convert the angular acceleration into the proper units of rad/s.

$$\alpha = \frac{1\ rev}{(1\ min)^2}\left(\frac{6.28\ rad}{1\ rev}\right)\left(\frac{1\ min}{60\ s}\right)^2 = 0.00174\ rad/s^2$$

The torque is equal to the angular acceleration multiplied by the rotational inertia we calculated in the previous example.

$$\tau = I\alpha = (0.01\ kg{\cdot}m^2)(1.74\ x\ 10^{-3}\ rad/s^2) = 1.74\ x\ 10^{-5}\ N{\cdot}m$$

◆ ◆ ◆

Problems

1. Find the size and direction of the change in velocity for each of the following initial and final velocities.
   a. 3 m/s south to 5 m/s south.
   b. 5 m/s south to 3 m/s south.
   c. 3 m/s south to 5 m/s north.
   d. 3 m/s south to 5 m/s west.

2. What is the change in velocity for each of the following initial and final velocities?
   a. 60 km/h forward to 100 km/h forward.
   b. 60 km/h forward to 100 km/h backward.
   c. 60 km/h forward to 100 km/h to the right.

3. An airplane was initially flying north with a speed of 100 mph. Later it was observed flying west at the same speed. What was its change in velocity? If the change occurred in 100 s, what was the average acceleration?

4. A car is driving north at 90 km/h when it turns so that it is driving northwest at 100 km/h. If this takes place in 30 s, what is the average acceleration of the car?

5. A cyclist turns a corner with a radius of 20 m at a speed of 20 m/s.
   a. What is the cyclist's acceleration?
   b. If the cyclist and cycle have a combined mass of 80 kg, what is the force causing them to turn?

6. A 60-kg person on a merry-go-round is traveling in a circle with a radius of 2 m at a speed of 4 m/s.
   a. What acceleration does the person experience?

   b. What is the centripetal force? How does it compare to the person's weight?

7. Our moon has a nearly circular orbit with a radius of 3.84×10^8 m and a speed of 1.02×10^3 m/s.
   a. What is the moon's acceleration?
   b. If the moon's mass is 7.35×10^{22} kg, what force does the earth exert on the moon?

8. A satellite orbiting the earth at a radius of 6500 km has a speed of 7.8 km/s.
   a. What is the acceleration of the satellite? How does this compare to the acceleration of the satellite if it were at rest just above the earth's surface?
   b. If the satellite has a mass of 1000 kg, what is the net force acting on it?

9. A baseball is hit with a horizontal speed of 20 m/s and a vertical speed of 15 m/s upward. What are these speeds 1 s later?

10. What are the horizontal and vertical speeds of the baseball in the previous question two seconds after it is hit?

11. An ashtray slides across a table with a speed of 1.2 m/s and falls off the edge. If it takes 0.4 s to reach the floor, how far from the edge of the table does it land?

12. A car drives off a vertical cliff at a speed of 27 m/s (60 mph). If it takes 4 s for it to hit the ground, how far from the base of the cliff does it land?

13. A ball is thrown horizontally at a speed of 5 m/s over level ground.
    a. If it starts out at a height of 19.6 m, how long does it take for the ball to reach the ground?
    b. How far will it move horizontally in this time?

14. A truck traveling at 20 m/s drives off a vertical cliff that is 78.5 m high.
    a. How long does it take to reach the level plain below?
    b. How far from the base of the cliff will it land?

15. A ball is launched horizontally at a speed of 40 m/s. With what speed will it hit the ground if it falls for 3 s?

16. A stunt car drives off the top of a parking garage at 30 m/s. How fast will it be going just before it hits that crash pad if it falls for 2 s?

17. A human cannonball is launched so that he has horizontal and vertical speeds of 9.81 m/s.
    a. How long does it take him to reach the top of his path?
    b. How far away should he place the safety net?

18. A football is thrown with a vertical speed of 9.81 m/s and a horizontal speed of 15 m/s. How far down field should the wide receiver be to catch this pass?

19. What torque does a 150-N salmon exert on a 2-m long fishing pole if the pole is horizontal and the salmon is out of the water?

20. A pirate with a mass of 90 kg stands on the end of a plank that extends 3 m beyond the gunwale. What torque is

need to keep him from falling into the water?

21. If the rotational speed of a flywheel changes from 80 rev/s to 89 rev/s in a time of 30 s, what is its average rotational acceleration?

22. If a phonograph turntable takes 2 s to reach its rotational speed of 33 rpm, what is its average rotational acceleration?

23. If a videodisc player can accelerate videodiscs at a rotational acceleration of 10 rev/s^2, how fast will it be rotating after 3 s?

24. If the wheel on a car accelerates from rest at a constant rate of 1.2 rev/s^2, how fast will it be turning after 12 s?

*25. If a merry-go-round starts from rest and accelerates at a constant rate of 10 rev/min^2, how many times will it rotate in 5 min?

*26. An amusement park ride accelerates from rest at a constant rate of 0.01 rev/s^2. How many times will it have rotated in 30 s?

27. What is the rotational acceleration of a wheel if it has a torque of 500 N·m and a rotational inertia of 200 kg·m^2?

*28. A uniform, solid wheel has a radius of 1.5 m and a mass of 20 kg. A string is wrapped around the outside of the wheel and a 1-kg mass is hung from its end. What is the rotational acceleration of the wheel?

29. What is the rotational inertia of a thin ring about its center if it has a mass of 8 kg and a radius of 0.5 m?

30. A solid sphere has a mass of 22 kg and a radius of 0.3 m. What is its rotational inertia about its center?

4 GRAVITY

4.1 Newton's Gravity

We can calculate the acceleration of the moon using the expression for centripetal acceleration developed in Sec 3.2. We begin with the measurement of the distance between the center of the earth and the center of the moon. If we make the very good approximation that the moon's orbit is circular, this is the radius r of the orbit. From this measurement we can obtain the circumference C of the orbit, that is, the distance traveled in one revolution.

$$C = 2\pi r = 2 \ (3.14) \ (3.84 \times 10^8 \ m) = 2.41 \times 10^9 \ m$$

Next we need the time to complete one revolution, the moon's period. In order to end up with units of m/s^2, we convert the time to seconds.

$$T = 27.3 \ days \left[\frac{24 \ hrs}{1 \ day}\right]\left[\frac{60 \ min}{1 hr}\right]\left[\frac{60 \ s}{1 \ min}\right] = 2.36 \times 10^6 \ s$$

The average speed v is computed from the distance traveled during one revolution divided by the period.

$$v = \frac{d}{t} = \frac{C}{T} = \frac{2.41 \times 10^9 \ m}{2.36 \times 10^6 \ s} = 1.02 \times 10^3 \ m/s$$

And, finally, we can calculate the centripetal acceleration a.

$$a = \frac{v^2}{r} = \frac{(1.02 \times 10^3 \ m/s)^2}{3.84 \times 10^8 \ m} = 2.71 \times 10^{-3} \ m/s^2$$

4.2 Using the Law of Universal Gravitation

Example 4.2.1

What is the gravitational force exerted on the earth by the sun?

Using the masses of the earth M_E and the sun M_S and the earth-sun distance R_{ES} given in the Appendix of this manual, we have

$$F = G\frac{M_E M_S}{R_{ES}^2}$$

$$F = \left(6.67 \times 10^{-11} \frac{N \cdot m^2}{kg^2}\right) \frac{(5.98 \times 10^{24}\, kg)(1.99 \times 10^{30}\, kg)}{(1.50 \times 10^{11}\, m)^2} = 3.53 \times 10^{22}\, N$$

Although this is a very large force, the mass of the earth is so large that the force produces a very small acceleration.

$$a = \frac{F}{m} = \frac{3.53 \times 10^{22}\, N}{5.98 \times 10^{24}\, kg} = 5.90 \times 10^{-3}\, m/s^2$$

Practice[1]

What acceleration does the sun have due to the force of the earth?

◆ ◆ ◆

4.3 The Value of G

We can obtain the mass of the earth by equating the weight of an object of mass m near the earth's surface with the gravitational force obtained from Newton's equation.

$$F = mg = \frac{GmM_e}{R_e^2}$$

where M_e is the earth's mass and R_e is the earth's radius. Canceling the object's mass m from both sides of the equation and solving for the mass of the earth, we obtain

$$M_e = \frac{gR_e^2}{G} = \frac{(9.81\, m/s^2)(6.37 \times 10^6\, m)^2}{6.67 \times 10^{-11}\, N \cdot m^2/kg^2} = 5.97 \times 10^{24}\, kg$$

4.4 Gravity Near the Earth's Surface

We can calculate the value of g near the earth's surface using the law of universal gravitation and the values for the earth's mass and radius.

---

[1] $1.77 \times 10^{-8}\, m/s^2$

$$g = \frac{F}{m} = G\frac{M_E m}{R_E^2 m} = G\frac{M_E}{R_E^2}$$

$$= 6.67 \times 10^{-11} \frac{N\cdot m^2}{kg^2} \frac{5.98 \times 10^{24}\ kg}{(6.37 \times 10^6\ m)^2} = 9.83\ \frac{N}{kg} = 9.83\ m/s^2$$

4.5 Satellites

Because the orbits of many earth-orbiting satellites are nearly circular and we know how to calculate the centripetal forces and accelerations for circular paths (Section 3.2), we'll restrict ourselves to circular orbits. This allows us to calculate the force exerted on the satellite of mass m in two ways. We begin by writing down the expression for the centripetal force required to maintain a satellite in a circular orbit of radius r with a speed v.

$$F = \frac{mv^2}{r}$$

Then we write down the expression for the gravitational force exerted by the earth on the satellite.

$$F = G\frac{mM_E}{r^2}$$

We can set these two expressions for the force equal to each other because the gravitational force is the centripetal force needed to make the satellite stay in its orbit. After canceling an m and one r on each side of the equation, we arrive at an expression for the square of the speed of the satellite in a circular orbit of radius r.

$$v^2 = G\frac{M_E}{r}$$

Note that this result does not depend on the mass of the satellite. All satellites with this orbital radius must have this speed squared.

Now that we have the speed of the satellite, we can calculate how long it takes to go around once, a time known as its *period T*. Because the satellite must travel a distance equal to the circumference C of the circular orbit, its period is given by

$$T = \frac{C}{v} = \frac{2\pi r}{v}$$

To obtain an alternate expression for the period, we can replace v by our previous result to obtain

$$T = 2\pi \sqrt{\frac{r^3}{GM_E}}$$

For all satellites orbiting the same central body, the periods and radii of the orbits all obey the relationship

$$T^2 = kr^3$$

where k is a constant. This was first discovered by Kepler and is now known as Kepler's third law.

This expression tells us that the period of the satellite increases as the orbital radius increases. This makes sense as we already know that the moon has a lot longer period than the Space Shuttle.

Example 4.5.1

What speed must a satellite have in order to be in orbit just above the surface of the earth?

We can use our expression if we neglect the obvious air resistance.

$$v^2 = G\frac{M_E}{r} = 6.67 \times 10^{-11} \frac{N \cdot m^2}{kg^2} \frac{5.98 \times 10^{24}\, kg}{6.37 \times 10^6\, m} = 6.26 \times 10^7\, m^2/s^2$$

We can obtain v by taking the square root.

$$v = 7910\, m/s = 7.91\, km/s$$

Note that this is consistent with the value of 8 km/s as stated in the text.

Practice[2]

What is the speed of a satellite in a circular orbit 500 km above the surface of the earth?

Example 4.5.2

How long would it take a satellite near the earth's surface to orbit the earth?

$$T = \frac{2\pi r}{v} = \frac{2(3.14)(6.37 \times 10^6\, m)}{7.91 \times 10^3\, m/s^2} = 5060\, s = 84.3\, min$$

---

[2] 7620 m/s

Practice[3]

What is the period (in minutes) of a satellite with an altitude of 500 km?

Example 4.5.3

What is the altitude of a geosynchronis satellite that has a period of 24 h?

We begin by taking our equation for the period given above and solving it for the radius. Divide both sides by 2π and then square the result.

$$T = 2\pi \sqrt{\frac{r^3}{GM_E}}$$

$$\frac{T^2}{4\pi^2} = \frac{r^3}{GM_E}$$

Multiplying both sides by GM_E, we obtain

$$r^3 = \frac{GM_E T^2}{4\pi^2}$$

$$= \frac{(6.67 \times 10^{-11} \frac{N \cdot m^2}{kg^2})(5.98 \times 10^{24} \, kg)(8.64 \times 10^4 \, s)^2}{39.5}$$

$$= 7.54 \times 10^{22} \, m^3$$

$$r = 4.22 \times 10^7 \, m = 42,200 \, km$$

This is the distance above the center of the earth, so we must subtract the radius of the earth to obtain the altitude of 35,800 km.

◆ ◆ ◆

4.6 The Field Concept

The gravitational field at a point in space is defined as the force an object would experience at that point, divided by the mass of the object. It is the force per unit mass. Since the field has the units of acceleration, the vector symbol *g* is often used to represent it. Once we know

---

[3] 94.4 min

the field, the force (including its direction) acting on an object of mass *m* located at that point is just *mg*.

Example 4.6.1

What is the gravitational field of the sun at the location of the earth?

The size of the field can be calculated by using the earth as the test object and dividing the gravitational force on the earth by the earth's mass. Since this is exactly the calculation that we did near the end of Example 4.2.1, the result is 5.90×10^{-3} N/kg directed toward the sun. It is important to realize that we could have used any object for this calculation. The value of the field would be the same.

Practice[4]

What is the gravitation field due to the earth at the location of the moon?

♦ ♦ ♦

Problems

Astronomical data is provided in the Appendix of this manual.

1. What is the acceleration of earth in its orbit about the sun?
2. What is the centripetal acceleration of Mars?
3. With what acceleration does Jupiter orbit the sun?
4. What is the centripetal acceleration of Pluto?
5. What gravitational force does the sun exert on Mars?
6. What gravitational forces does Venus exert on the sun?
7. How does the maximum gravitational force that Jupiter exerts on the earth compare to the gravitational force the sun exerts on the earth?

8. How does the gravitational force earth exerts on the moon compare to the average gravitational force the sun exerts on the moon?
9. Two objects released from rest in a region of space where there is no net external gravitational force accelerate toward each other. If one object accelerates 9 times as much as the other, how do their masses compare?
10. Two objects in outer space accelerate toward each other under the influence of their mutual gravitational attraction. If one object has twice the mass of the other, how do their accelerations compare?

---

[4] 2.72×10^{-3} N/kg as calculated in Section 4.1

11. The gravitational force on a synchronous satellite is only 2.5% of its weight on earth. What is the gravitational force on a 1-kg mass in the satellite?

12. What is the gravitational force on a 1-kg mass in the Space Shuttle when it is 200 km above the earth's surface? Assume that the earth's radius is 6400 km.

*13. The radius of Venus' orbit is 0.7 times that of the earth and its mass is 0.8 times the earth's mass. How does the sun's gravitational force on Venus compare to its force on the earth?

*14. The mass of Mars is 0.1 times that of the earth and the radius of its orbit is 1.5 times that of the earth. How does Mars' gravitational force on the sun compare to that of the earth on the sun?

*15. Jupiter is 5.2 times as far away from the sun as the earth and it has 318 times the mass of the earth. Will Jupiter exert more or less force on the sun than the earth does?

*16. Given that the average distance of the moon from the sun is 390 times the distance between the earth and the moon and that the mass of the sun is 33,300 times that of earth, what is the ratio of the forces exerted on the moon by the earth and the sun?

17. If 1-kg mass on the moon has a weight of 1.62 N, what is the mass of the moon?

18. If the acceleration due to gravity on the surface of Mars is 3.73 m/s^2, what is the mass of Mars?

19. An astronaut on a strange planet has a mass of 80 kg and a weight of 240 N. What is the value of the acceleration due to gravity on this planet?

20. In a science fiction story several astronauts visit a strange planet known as K3 that is orbiting a nearby star. They decide to weigh a block with a known mass of 20 kg. If they obtain a weight of 80 N, what is the acceleration due to gravity on the surface of K3?

21. What is the acceleration due to gravity on the surface of the moon?

22. What is the value of the acceleration due to gravity on Mercury?

*23. The radius of Mars is about 0.5 times the earth's radius and its mass is 0.1 times the earth's mass. What would you expect for the value of the acceleration of gravity on the surface of Mars?

*24. The mass of Venus is 80% that of the earth while its radius is 95% that of the earth. What is the value of the acceleration due to gravity on Venus?

25. What is the orbital velocity of a satellite with an orbital radius equal to twice the radius of the earth?

26. What is the orbital velocity of a satellite orbiting the moon near its surface?

27. What is the orbital period of the satellite in Problem 25?

28. What is the orbital period of the satellite in Problem 26?

*29. If the rotational period of Mars is 24.6 h, how high would a satellite have to be in order to orbit Mars once each Martian day?

4 Gravity

*30. Mercury has a rotational period of 58.6 days. How high would a satellite have to be in order to orbit Mercury once each Mercurian day?

31. What is the value of the earth's gravitational field at a distance equal to twice the earth's radius?

32. What is the value of the sun's gravitational field at its surface?

5   MOMENTUM

5.1   Changing an Object's Momentum

An object's momentum is changed by an impulse, a force acting for a time interval, according to the expression that we obtained from Newton's second law.

$$\Delta(mv) = F_{net}\,t$$

When using this expression, we must remember that momentum and impulse are both vectors. For the case of motion along a straight line, we can once again use plus and minus signs to indicate direction.

Example 5.1.1

What is the change in the momentum of a freely falling ball with a mass of 1 kg during each second of fall?

We obtain the change in momentum by looking at the impulse exerted on the ball by the force of gravity, that is, the ball's weight.

$$\Delta(mv) = F_{net}\,t = (9.81\,N)(1\,s) = 9.81\,N{\cdot}s = 9.81\,kg{\cdot}m/s$$

Since we know that the velocity of an object in free fall changes by 9.81 m/s during each second, we can check our result by calculating the change in momentum directly. Because the mass of the ball doesn't change, the change in momentum is simply given by the mass times the change in velocity.

$$\Delta(mv) = m\Delta v = (1\,kg)(9.81\,m/s) = 9.81\,kg{\cdot}m/s$$

Example 5.1.2

A 1500-kg car is initially traveling at 30 m/s. If the frictional force is constant at 10,000 N, how long will it take the car to stop?

We can solve our equation for the time t and plug in the given values to obtain our answer.

$$t = \frac{\Delta(mv)}{F_{net}} = \frac{m(v_f - v_i)}{F_{net}} = \frac{(1500\,kg)(0 - 30\,m/s)}{-10,000\,N} = 4.5\,s$$

Note that we used a negative value for the frictional force as it was acting in the direction opposite to the velocity.

Practice[1]

How long would it take the car to stop if the maximum frictional force were only 5,000 N?

◆ ◆ ◆

5.2 Using Conservation of Linear Momentum

Conservation of linear momentum holds whenever there is no net external force acting on a system. This means that the total momentum of all parts of the system must be the same before and after an interaction. In computing the total momentum of a system, we must be very careful to include the direction of each momentum. For motion along a straight line, the direction can be indicated by a plus or minus sign.

Example 5.2.1

Let's assume that a 50-kg woman is standing still on a 10-kg giant skateboard. If she then walks to the right at 1 m/s, what is the resulting velocity of the skateboard?

Begin by choosing the direction to the right as positive. We then set the total momentum of the woman and the skateboard equal to the initial momentum. It is zero in this case.

$$m_b v_b + m_w v_w = 0$$

where the subscripts b and w refer to the board and woman, respectively. We can now solve the equation for the velocity of the board and plug in the given values.

$$v_b = -v_w \frac{m_w}{m_b} = -1\,m/s\,\frac{50\,kg}{10\,kg} = -5\,m/s$$

where the minus sign indicates that the board is moving in the negative direction, that is, to the left. This answer makes sense; because the board has one-fifth the mass, it needs 5 times the velocity to have the same momentum as the woman.

Practice[2]

What is the velocity of the board if the woman is replaced by a man with a mass of 80 kg?

---

[1] 9 s

[2] -8 m/s

Example 5.2.2

Let's repeat the previous example for the case when the board and the woman have an initial velocity of 6 m/s to the right.

We once again set the final momentum equal to the initial momentum. Let's use the subscript *i* for the initial values. The woman's velocity is now 1 m/s faster than that of the board, or 7 m/s.

$$m_b v_b + m_w v_w = (m_b + m_w) v_i$$

$$
\begin{aligned}
v_b &= \frac{(m_b + m_w) v_i - m_w v_w}{m_b} \\
&= \frac{(60\ kg)(6\ m/s) - (50\ kg)(7\ m/s)}{10\ kg} \\
&= \frac{10\ kg \cdot m/s}{10\ kg} = 1\ m/s
\end{aligned}
$$

Therefore, the board slows down to 1 m/s, but it is still traveling to the right.

Practice[3]

What is the final velocity of the board if the initial velocity is only 4 m/s?

◆   ◆   ◆

5.3 Accident Investigations

Example 5.3.1

If a 1500-kg car traveling at 30 m/s undergoes a head-on collision with a 4500-kg truck traveling in the opposite direction at 20 m/s, what is the final velocity of the two if they wind up as one big heap?

Let's begin by calculating the total momentum p_i before the crash. Choosing the direction of the truck's velocity as positive, we have

$$
\begin{aligned}
p_i &= m_c v_c + m_t v_t \\
&= (1500\ kg)(-30\ m/s) + (4500\ kg)(20\ m/s) = 45{,}000\ kg \cdot m/s
\end{aligned}
$$

This must be equal to the final momentum p_f of the total mass.

---

[3] -1 m/s

$$p_f = (m_c + m_t)\, v_f = p_i$$

$$v_f = \frac{p_i}{m_c + m_t} = \frac{45{,}000 \; kg \cdot m/s}{6000 \; kg} = 7.5 \; m/s$$

The two move in the truck's original direction.

♦   ♦   ♦

5.4   A Two-Dimensional Crash

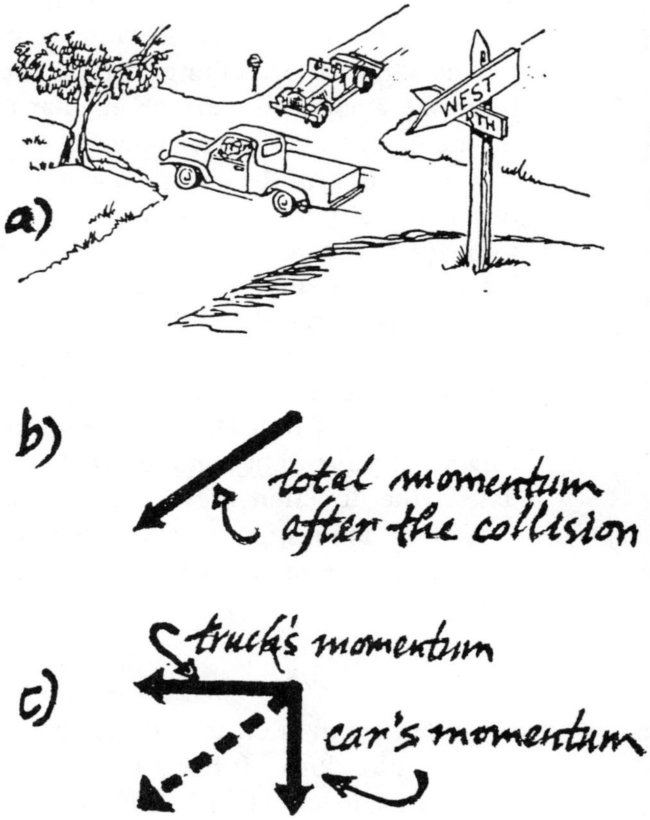

Example 5.4.1

Suppose that a westbound, 1000-kg car collides with a northbound, 2000-kg pickup truck as shown in Fig. 5.4.1 (a). The direction of the total momentum just after the collision is shown in the diagram of Fig. 5.4.1 (b). If the total momentum after the collision was 50,000 kg·m/s, how fast was each vehicle moving before the collision?

We make a scale drawing where ½ cm represents 10,000 kg·m/s. We know that the momenta of the two cars before the crash must add together as vectors to give their total momentum after the crash. This can only be done in one way. The initial momenta must be the west and north components of the final momentum as shown in Fig. 5.4.1 (c). Measurement of the lengths of these components indicates that the car's momentum was 30,000 kg·m/s and the pickup's was 40,000 kg·m/s. Since the mass of the car is 1000 kg, its velocity was

Fig. 5.4.1

$$v = \frac{p}{m} = \frac{30{,}000 \; kg \cdot m/s}{1000 \; kg} = 30 \; m/s$$

Similarly, the velocity of the pickup was 20 m/s. If the speed limit was 25 m/s, the car was speeding.

♦   ♦   ♦

5.5 Conservation of Angular Momentum

Angular momentum is also a vector, but its direction is not intuitively obvious. The first vectors that we discussed seemed reasonable because in each case the direction of the vector was obvious. A force to the right is represented by a vector pointing to the right; the velocity vector points in the direction that the object is moving. The direction of the acceleration vector is not as intuitive as it doesn't usually point in the direction the particle is moving, but it always points in the direction of the net force. In uniform circular motion, for example, the acceleration points toward the center of the circle -- perpendicular to the velocity vector. In projectile motion, the acceleration always points vertically downward.

Let's look at something that has a constant angular momentum to see how a direction might be associated with the angular momentum vector. Consider a ball whirling in a circle on the end of a string as shown in Fig. 3-1 in the text. If the speed of the ball is constant and the length of the string stays the same, the angular momentum is constant. The directions of the velocity and acceleration vectors are continually changing and therefore cannot be used to describe a constant angular momentum. However, there is a direction that is constant. This is the line that passes through the center of the circular path and perpendicular to the plane of the circle.

There is still a problem of uniqueness. The vector can be aligned along this axis but point in one of two directions. A vector must be unique to describe a particular motion. If it doesn't, it is of little value. The specific choice is arbitrary; the convention is to curl the fingers of your <u>right hand</u> along the direction of motion. Your thumb then points along the axis in the direction of the angular momentum as shown in Fig. 5-12 in the text.

Conservation of angular momentum requires that the direction of the angular momentum as well as its size remain constant. In many cases, the direction remains constant and we need only work with the magnitude.

Example 5.5.1

> The earth is closest to the sun in January (147 million km) and farthest in July (152 million km). It has a known speed of 28.8 km/s when it is farthest from the sun. What is its speed when it is closest?
>
> Because the force on the earth is always directed toward the sun, there is no torque on earth and its angular momentum is conserved. At the locations on the orbit when the earth is closest to and farthest from the sun, the velocity is perpendicular to the radius and the calculation of the angular momentum is easy because the moment arm is equal to the distance from the sun. Using the subscripts *f* for farthest and *n* for nearest, we have
>
> $$mr_n v_n = mr_f v_f$$

We can cancel the mass m of the earth and solve the relationship for any one of the remaining quantities. Solving for v_n and substituting the given values for the others, we have

$$v_n = v_f \frac{r_f}{r_n} = (28.8 \; km/s) \frac{1.52 \times 10^8 \; km}{1.47 \times 10^8 \; km} = 29.8 \; km/s$$

Example 5.5.2

If a diver can execute a somersault in the tuck position in 1 s, how long would it take in the layout position?

Let's assume that we use the values given in Fig. 5-10 in the text. Then the relative values for the rotational inertia are 230 and 830 for the tuck and layout positions, respectively. Conservation of angular momentum requires that

$$I_\ell \omega_\ell = I_t \omega_t$$

where I_ℓ and I_t are the rotational inertia for the layout and tuck positions and ω_ℓ and ω_t are the corresponding angular speeds in rad/s. Because $\omega = 2\pi f$, we can also express this in terms of the frequency f.

$$I_\ell f_\ell = I_t f_t$$

Solving for f_ℓ, we obtain

$$f_\ell = f_t \frac{I_t}{I_\ell} = 1 \frac{rev}{s} \left(\frac{230}{830} \right) = 0.277 \; rev/s$$

Therefore, the time needed to complete the somersault in the layout position is

$$T = \frac{1}{f_\ell} = \frac{1}{0.277 \; rev/s} = 3.61 \; s$$

Practice[4]

Given that the relative rotational inertia for the pike position is 340, how long would a somersault in the pike position require?

◆ ◆ ◆

---

[4] 1.48 s

Problems

1. A rocket car with a mass of 1000 kg develops a constant thrust of 20,000 N. If we can neglect the mass of the expended fuel, what are the momentum and speed of the car at the end of 3.0 s?

2. A model rocket has a weight of 1.0 N and develops an average thrust of 5.0 N. What are its momentum and speed at the end of 2 s? (Assume that the mass of fuel expelled is negligible.)

3. A 1600-kg car is traveling at 20 m/s when the driver takes her foot off the gas pedal. If we assume that the frictional forces are constant at 800 N, how long will it take the car to stop?

4. If the driving force on a 1400-kg car is a constant 1500 N, how long will it take for the car to reach 30 m/s from rest?

5. Let's assume that the collision of a car with a wall takes 0.1 s. If the driver has a mass of 70 kg and is traveling at 24 m/s, what is the average force exerted on the driver by the seat belt? How does this compare to the driver's weight?

6. If the driver in the previous problem uses an air bag to increase the collision time to 1 s, what is the average force?

*7. Assume that a man with a mass of 80 kg jumps from an airplane without a parachute and hits a snow bank with a terminal speed of 50 m/s. What collision time would be needed for him to experience an average force no larger than ten times his weight?

*8. A car traveling at 30 m/s crashes causing air bags to inflate in front of the passengers. What minimum collision time must be provided by the air bags in order for the average forces on the passengers to remain less than their weights?

9. A toy cannon with a mass of 5 kg fires a 0.2-kg ball with a horizontal velocity of 3 m/s. What is the recoil speed of the cannon?

10. A 30-kg boy standing on roller skates throws a 0.5-kg ball with a horizontal velocity of 15 m/s. What is the recoil speed of the boy?

11. A man with a mass of 80-kg running at a speed of 5 m/s jumps onto a stationary skateboard with a mass of 4 kg. What is their combined speed?

12. A woman with a mass of 50 kg is riding on a giant 10-kg skateboard at a speed of 6 m/s. If she jumps off the board in the backward direction at a speed of 3 m/s *relative to the skateboard*, what is the final speed of the board?

13. A 2-kg ball traveling to the right with a speed of 6 m/s collides with a 4-kg ball traveling to the left with a speed of 4 m/s. If the 2-kg ball recoils to the left at 1 m/s, what is the velocity of the 4-kg ball after the collision?

14. A 2-kg ball traveling to the right with a speed of 4 m/s collides with a 4-kg ball traveling to the left with a speed of 2 m/s. After the collision the 2-kg ball travels to the left at 2 m/s. What is the velocity of the 4-kg ball after the collision?

15. Assume that a stationary car is struck by another car with the same mass. The two cars stick together and move with one-half the original velocity of the moving car. Is momentum conserved in this collision?

16. A moving ball stops when it collides head-on with a stationary ball having the same mass. The stationary ball leaves with a velocity equal to that of the incoming ball. This is not the only possibility allowed by the law of conservation of momentum. What are some of the other possibilities?

17. A 1000-kg car traveling north at 30 m/s collides with a 1500-kg car traveling west at 20 m/s. If they stick together, what is the final momentum of the cars?

18. A 1200-kg car traveling west at 25 m/s collides with and sticks to a 1400-kg car traveling south at 30 m/s. What is the final momentum of the cars?

19. A 1000-kg car traveling north at 30 m/s collides with a 1400-kg car traveling east. If the cars lock bumpers and travel directly northeast after the collision, how fast was the 1400-kg car traveling?

20. A 1200-kg car traveling west at 20 m/s collides with a 2400-kg truck traveling south. If they stick together and leave the accident traveling 60° south of west, what was the speed of the truck? (Hint: make a scale drawing.)

21. The closest Mars gets to the sun is 207 million km and its farthest distance away is 249 million km. If Mars' orbital speed at closest approach is 26.5 km/s, what is its orbital speed when it is farthest away?

22. Halley's comet orbits the sun in a huge elliptical path. Its greatest distance from the sun is 60 times the smallest distance. If the comet has a speed of 193,000 km/h when it is nearest the sun, what is its speed when it is farthest away?

23. A metal ring has a mass of 12 kg and a radius of 0.50 m. If it is rotating about its axis at 5 rpm, what is its angular momentum?

24. A solid, uniform disc has a mass of 8 kg and a radius of 0.20 m. What is its angular momentum when it is rotating at 30 degrees/s? (See Fig. 3.5.1 for the rotational inertia.)

25. A solid cylindrical disk is rotating at 50 rev/min with its axle pointing vertically. An identical disk with no rotation is dropped directly onto the rotating disk. What is the final rotational speed of the two disks?

26. An ice skater is spinning with a rotational speed of 1 rev/s. When he extends his arms and legs, his rotational inertia increases by a factor of three. What is his final rotational speed?

27. Show that the units of momentum and impulse are the same.

28. Show that the units of angular momentum are the same as those of torque multiplied by time.

6 ENERGY

6.1 Energy of Motion

Example 6.1.1

How does the kinetic energy of a bullet fired from a rifle compare to the kinetic energy of a baseball thrown by a major league pitcher?

Before we can begin to answer this question, we need to have some additional data. The mass of a 30-06 bullet is about 0.01 kg and the muzzle velocity is about 900 m/s (2000 mph). An official baseball must have a mass within a few grams of 145 g. Finally, a major league pitcher can throw the ball up to 45 m/s (100 mph).

Let's begin by calculating the kinetic energy KE_b of the bullet.

$$KE_b = \frac{1}{2} m_b v_b^2 = \frac{1}{2}(0.01\ kg)(900\ m/s)^2 = 4050\ J$$

The kinetic energy KE_B of the baseball is

$$KE = \frac{1}{2} m v^2 = \frac{1}{2}(0.145\ kg)(45\ m/s)^2 = 147\ J$$

To compare the two kinetic energies, we divide them.

$$\frac{KE_b}{KE_B} = \frac{4050\ J}{147\ J} = 27.6$$

Therefore, the bullet has almost 27 times the kinetic energy.

We can also compare the two kinetic energies directly without calculating each one separately. This often has the advantage that the units cancel directly as long as the same type of quantity is measured in a consistent set of units.

$$\frac{KE_b}{KE_B} = \frac{\frac{1}{2} m_b v_b^2}{\frac{1}{2} m_B v_B^2} = \left(\frac{m_b}{m_B}\right)\left(\frac{v_b}{v_B}\right)^2 = \left(\frac{10\ g}{145\ g}\right)\left(\frac{2000\ mph}{100\ mph}\right)^2 = 27.6$$

Practice[1]

What is the ratio of the kinetic energies if the bullet has half the speed?

---

[1] 6.9

6.2 Conservation of Kinetic Energy

As discussed in the text, not all collisions are elastic. Any collision in which the objects stick together after the collision is totally inelastic and the maximum amount of kinetic energy is lost that is allowed by the conservation of momentum. However, many collisions are intermediate in that some kinetic energy is lost, but not the maximum amount.

Example 6.2.1

A 0.5-kg ball falls from a height of 45 m, hits the ground, and bounces to a height of 20 m. What fraction of its kinetic energy is lost in the collision?

According to the Table in Sec. 1.7, a ball falling from a height of 45 m takes 3 s to hit the ground and is traveling with a speed of 30 m/s. The same Table shows that ball falling from 20 m will hit the ground at 20 m/s after 2 s. Since free fall is symmetric, the ball must have left the ground with a speed of 20 m/s. This information allows us to calculate the two kinetic energies.

$$KE_i = \frac{1}{2}mv_i^2 = \frac{1}{2}(0.5\,kg)(30\,m/s)^2 = 225\,J$$

$$KE_i = \frac{1}{2}mv_i^2 = \frac{1}{2}(0.5\,kg)(20\,m/s)^2 = 100\,J$$

Therefore, the fractional loss in kinetic energy is

$$\frac{KE_i - KE_f}{KE_i} = \frac{225\,J - 100\,J}{225\,J} = 0.556 = 55.6\%$$

The fractional loss can be calculated more directly without calculating the individual kinetic energies first.

$$\frac{KE_i - KE_f}{KE_i} = \frac{\frac{1}{2}mv_i^2 - \frac{1}{2}mv_f^2}{\frac{1}{2}mv_i^2} = \frac{v_i^2 - v_f^2}{v_i^2} = 1 - \left(\frac{v_f}{v_i}\right)^2$$

$$= 1 - \left(\frac{20\,m/s}{30\,m/s}\right)^2 = 1 - 0.444 = 0.556$$

This last relationship has the nice feature of showing us that the fractional loss in kinetic energy does not depend on the mass of the ball.

Practice[2]

What is the fractional loss in kinetic energy if the ball rebounds to a height of 5 m?

◆ ◆ ◆

6.3 Changing Kinetic Energy

We can show how work changes the kinetic energy of an object by using Newton's second law to write the force as the product of the mass and the acceleration.

$$W = Fd = mad$$

The kinetic energy depends on the object's speed, so we modify this expression by making two substitutions that eventually get speed into the equation. In Chapter 1 in the text we found that under the action of a constant force, an object <u>starting from rest</u> moves a distance given by

$$d = \frac{1}{2}at^2$$

Using this relation, our expression becomes

$$W = mad = ma(\frac{1}{2}at^2) = \frac{1}{2}m(at)^2$$

We also learned in Chapter 1 that

$$v_f = v_i + at$$

Since v_i is zero in this case, $v_f = at$. Therefore, we can replace the term in parentheses by v_f to obtain

$$W = \frac{1}{2}mv_f^2$$

This equation says that the work done on the box is equal to the kinetic energy it acquires. Since the box started with zero kinetic energy, this equation also represents the change in the kinetic energy due to the work done on the box. If the box had been given an initial velocity,

---

[2] 88.9%

the substitutions would have been a little more difficult, but the results would have been the same; the work done is equal to the change in the kinetic energy.

$$W = \Delta KE = \frac{1}{2}mv_f^2 - \frac{1}{2}mv_i^2$$

Example 6.3.1

How much work is required to accelerate a 1500-kg car from rest to a speed of 30 m/s?

Since the work is just equal to the change in kinetic energy,

$$W = \frac{1}{2}mv_f^2 - 0 = \frac{1}{2}(1600\,kg)(30\,m/s)^2 = 7.2 \times 10^5\,J$$

Practice[3]

How much work is require to accelerate the car to one-half this speed?

Example 6.3.2

How much work is required to accelerate a 1500-kg car from an initial speed of 15 m/s to a final speed of 30 m/s?

The work is equal to the change in kinetic energy.

$$
\begin{aligned}
W &= \frac{1}{2}mv_f^2 - \frac{1}{2}mv_i^2 \\
&= \frac{1}{2}(1600\,kg)(30\,m/s)^2 - \frac{1}{2}(1600\,kg)(15\,m/s)^2 \\
&= 7.2 \times 10^5\,J - 1.8 \times 10^5\,J = 5.4 \times 10^5\,J
\end{aligned}
$$

Example 6.3.3

What average force is required to accelerate a 6000-kg truck from rest to a final speed of 20 m/s over a distance of 1.5 km?

We can equate the work equal to the change in kinetic energy (the final kinetic energy in this case) and solve for the average force.

---

[3] $1.8 \times 10^5\,J$

$$Fd = \Delta KE = \frac{1}{2}mv_f^2$$

$$F = \frac{\frac{1}{2}mv_f^2}{d} = \frac{\frac{1}{2}(6000\ kg)(20\ m/s)^2}{1.5\ x\ 10^3\ m} = 800\ N$$

Practice[4]

What average force would be required for the truck to reach the same final speed in 0.5 km?

◆ ◆ ◆

6.4 Gravitational Energy

Example 6.4.1

How much gravitational potential energy does a 70-kg mountain climber gain when walking from sea level to the top of a 3000-m peak?

$$GPE = mgh = (70\ kg)(9.81\ m/s^2)(3000\ m) = 2.06\ x\ 10^6\ J$$

Notice that we did not need to specify how far the climber actually walked from the starting place to the top of the mountain. The change in gravitational potential energy depends on the change in vertical height.

Practice[5]

What is the gain in potential energy if the mountain climber starts at an elevation of 1000 m?

◆ ◆ ◆

6.5 Conservation of Mechanical Energy

Example 6.5.1

How fast does a 0.4-kg ball hit the ground when it is dropped from a height of 50 m?

---

[4] 2400 N

[5] 1.37 x 10^6 J

6 Energy

Conservation of mechanical energy tells us to set the final value of the mechanical energy equal to its initial value.

$$KE_f + GPE_f = KE_i + GPE_i$$

Let's choose the zero value for the gravitational potential energy to be zero at the ground level. Noting that the initial kinetic energy is zero, we have

$$KE_f = GPE_i$$

We can now substitute in the formulas for the kinetic energy and gravitational potential energy.

$$\frac{1}{2}mv_f^2 = mgh$$

Canceling the mass m and solving for v^2, we get our answer.

$$v^2 = 2gh = 2(9.81 \, m/s^2)(50 \, m) = 981 \, m^2/s^2$$

$$v = 31.3 \, m/s$$

We know that this answer is reasonable because the ball must be in the air for 3.13 s to obtain this speed and that a ball will fall 44.1 m from rest in 3 s. Notice also that the mass does not affect the final speed. This is what we expect for free fall.

Practice[6]

What is the speed if the ball is dropped from twice the height?

Example 6.5.2

A ball is shot from the top of a 50-m high cliff with a speed of 5 m/s. With what speed does it hit the plain below?

We set the gravitational potential energy equal to zero at the bottom of the cliff and equate the final value of the mechanical energy to its initial value.

$$\frac{1}{2}mv_f^2 + 0 = \frac{1}{2}mv_i^2 + mgh$$

Solving for v_f^2 and plugging in the given values yields

---

[6] 44.3 m/s

$$v_f = 31.7 \, m/s$$

Note that we did not need to know the direction of the ball to compute the final speed. The ball could have been launched straight up, at an angle upward, horizontal, or downward without affecting the result.

Practice

Show that you get the same answer by choosing the gravitational potential energy to be zero at the top of the cliff.

♦ ♦ ♦

6.6 Power

Example 6.6.1

What power is required to accelerate a 1500-kg car from rest to a speed of 30 m/s in a time of 6 s?

We already calculated in Example 6.3.1 that the car gained 7.2 x 10^5 J of kinetic energy. Therefore, the average power required is

$$P = \frac{\Delta E}{t} = \frac{7.2 \, x \, 10^5 \, J}{6 \, s} = 1.2 \, x \, 10^5 \, W = 120 \, kW$$

Practice[7]

What average power would be required in Example 6.3.2 if the change in speed takes place in 3 s?

♦ ♦ ♦

Problems

1. What is the kinetic energy of a 50-kg diver if she hits the water at 4 m/s?

2. If an 18-wheeler has a mass of 30,000 kg and a speed of 25 m/s, what is its kinetic energy?

---

[7] 180 kW

3. What is the speed of a 1000-kg sports car with a kinetic energy of 100,000 J?

4. If an 80-kg jogger has a kinetic energy of 1000 J, how fast is the jogger running?

5. A 1-kg air-hockey puck moving at 6 m/s collides head-on with a stationary 2-kg puck. The 1-kg puck recoils in the backward direction with a speed of 2 m/s while the 2-kg puck moves in the forward direction with a speed of 4 m/s. Are momentum and kinetic energy conserved in this collision?

6. A 1-kg air-hockey puck moving at 8 m/s collides head-on with 2-kg puck traveling at 4 m/s in the opposite direction. The pucks rebound in opposite directions with the 1-kg puck traveling at 6 m/s and the 2-kg puck at 3 m/s. Are momentum and kinetic energy conserved?

7. Assume that a stationary car is struck by an identical car. The two cars stick together and move with one-half the original velocity. Is kinetic energy conserved in this collision?

8. A moving air-hockey puck stops when it collides head-on with a stationary one. The stationary puck leaves with a velocity equal to that of the incoming puck. Show that this collision conserves both momentum and kinetic energy.

*9. A 1-kg air-hockey puck moving at 6 m/s collides head-on with a stationary 2-kg puck. If the two pucks stick together, what is their final kinetic energy?

*10. A 1-kg air-hockey puck moving at 5 m/s collides head-on with 2-kg puck traveling at 4 m/s in the opposite direction. What is their total kinetic energy after the collision if the two pucks stick together?

11. What average force is required for a sprinter with a mass of 75 kg to reach a speed of 10 m/s over a distance of 20 m?

12. What average force would it take to catch a 0.5-kg ball with a speed of 40 m/s if your hands give a distance of 25 cm?

13. A force of 0.2 N acts on a 0.4-kg air-hockey puck for a distance of 0.6 m. What is the final kinetic energy of the cart if it had an initial kinetic energy of 0.2 J?

14. A 0.5-kg air-hockey puck has an initial kinetic energy of 0.4 J. What will its final kinetic energy be after a force of 0.4 N acts on it for a distance of 0.2 m?

15. Use the data on page 123 in the text to calculate the braking distance for a car traveling at 45 mph.

16. Use the data on page 123 in the text to calculate the braking distance for a car traveling at 35 mph.

17. A bucket of water is raised from a well using a rope wrapped around a cylinder. The cylinder is turned by a crank that is 48 cm long. The handle follows a circle that has a circumference of 3 m. If the force on the crank is 100 N, how much work is done each time it goes around?

18. The handle of a grinding wheel goes around a circle with a circumference of 1 m. If it requires a force of 150 N to turn the handle at a steady rate, how much work is performed each revolution?

19. What is the change in gravitational potential energy of a 200-kg barbell if the weight lifter raises it 2.2 m?

20. If a 0.7-kg book falls from a 1.8-m high shelf, what is the book's change in gravitational potential energy?

21. A man with a mass of 80 kg falls 10 m. How much gravitational potential energy does he lose?

22. A ball that weighs 2 N can be placed on a counter that is 1 m above the floor or on a shelf that is 2 m above the floor.
    a. If we chose the zero value of gravitational potential energy to be at the floor, what is the value of the gravitational potential energy when it is on the counter? On the shelf?
    b. How much does the gravitational potential energy change when the ball is moved from the counter to the shelf?
    c. Do your answers to these questions change if the gravitational potential energy is chosen to be zero on the counter?

23. Show that the units of kinetic energy, work, and gravitational potential energy are the same.

24. Show that the kinetic energy of an object can be written $KE = p^2/2m$, where p is the object's momentum and m is its mass.

25. A man with a mass of 80 kg falls 10 m. How much kinetic energy does he gain?

26. A 30-kg child slides down a frictionless slide that is 3-m tall. What is the child's kinetic energy at the bottom of the slide?

27. What is the speed of a man who falls 9.81 m?

28. What is the speed of the child in problem 26 at the bottom of the slide?

29. What is the speed of a ball after it falls a distance of 44.1 m? Does this agree with the value in the Table in Section 1.7?

30. A pendulum bob changes height by a distance of 60 cm from one end of its swing to its lowest point. What is the speed of the pendulum at the lowest point?

31. A ball is hit vertically upward with a speed of 35 m/s. How high will it go?

*32. A model rocket weighs 1 N and develops an average thrust of 5 N for 2 s. At the end of this time, the rocket has obtained a height of 80 m and a speed of 80 m/s. (Neglect the loss in mass due to the expelled gases.)
    a. How much work was done by the net force on the rocket?
    b. Calculate the value of the kinetic energy of the rocket using the formula $\frac{1}{2}mv^2$.
    c. Should the answers to parts a and b be the same? Explain.
    d. How much higher will the rocket coast before this kinetic energy is converted to gravitational potential energy?

33. What average power is required for a runner with a mass of 70 kg to reach a speed of 8 m/s during a time of 1.5 s?

34. What average power is dissipated by the brakes of a 1600-kg car if comes to a stop from a speed of 30 m/s in 4 s?

35. What happened to the work in Problem 17 if the bucket is raised at a steady rate?

36. What happens to the work in Problem 18?

37. Show that the product of force and velocity has the units of power, not energy.

*38. A 1982 Lincoln Continental requires 16.5 hp (12.3 kW) to maintain a speed of 50 mph (22.4 m/s) on a level highway. This power is used to overcome friction and air resistance. What is the force required to maintain this speed? (See the previous problem for a hint.)

7 THE STRUCTURE OF MATTER

7.1 Masses and Sizes of Atoms

Oil floats on water and, given enough surface, can spread out making a very thin film. Oleic acid, a compound of hydrogen, carbon, and oxygen, does not mix with water and spreads out even better than oil. A single drop of oleic acid will cover the surface of an entire swimming pool. If we mix this compound with alcohol and put a single drop of the alcohol/acid mixture on water, we have a way of putting a very, very small amount of oleic acid on the water's surface. The alcohol evaporates very fast and the oleic acid is left on the water's surface. If we first sprinkle a fine flour on the water's surface, we see that the acid pushes the flour away as it spreads out into a circular shape. The flour gives us a way of measuring the size of the thin acid film.

Suppose we mix 1 part of oleic acid with 499 parts of alcohol. We then measure the volume of a single drop of this solution by putting a number of drops into a graduated beaker. The volume of the oleic acid by itself V_{acid} is the volume of the drop V_{drop} divided by 500.

If the experiment gives a circular pattern with a radius r, we can calculate the circle's area A using the relationship $A = \pi r^2$. This area is only due to the acid layer since the alcohol evaporates away. Multiplying the area by the height h of the thin film also gives the volume of the oleic acid. Setting the two volumes of oleic acid equal to each other gives a value for the height.

$$V_{acid} = \frac{V_{drop}}{500} = A h$$

The only unknown is the height h, so we can solve the equation for the height.

$$h = \frac{V_{acid}}{A} = \frac{V_{drop}}{500\, A}$$

This gives us an upper limit on the size of an oleic acid molecule as the layer must be at least one molecule thick.

Example 7.1.1

It takes 136 drops from our eye dropper to yield a volume of 6 cm^3. Therefore, a single drop of the alcohol/acid mixture has a volume of

$$V_{acid} = \frac{V_{drop}}{500} = \frac{6\ cm^3}{135 \times 500} = 8.8 \times 10^{-5}\ cm^3$$

If the experiment gives a circular pattern with a radius of 15 cm, the circle's area is 707 cm^2. What is the thickness of the layer?

$$h = \frac{V_{acid}}{A} = \frac{8.8 \times 10^{-5}\ cm^3}{707\ cm^2} = 1.2 \times 10^{-7}\ cm$$

Practice[1]

If the circular pattern was incorrectly measured and the 15 cm is actually the diameter of the circle, what is the height of the molecule?

◆ ◆ ◆

If we assume that the oleic acid molecule is roughly cubical, this height is also the width and length of the molecule. Cubing this number gives an estimate of the volume V of a single oleic acid molecule.

$$V = lwh = (1.2 \times 10^{-7}\ cm)^3 = 1.7 \times 10^{-21}\ cm^3$$

Dividing the molecular volume into the macroscopic volume gives the number of molecules N in our sample.

$$N = \frac{V_{acid}}{V/molecule} = \frac{8.8 \times 10^{-5}\ cm^3}{1.7 \times 10^{-21}\ cm^3/molecule} = 5.2 \times 10^{16}\ molecules$$

We can get the mass of the oleic acid molecule from its density. The density of the oleic acid is about 0.9 g/cm^3. Since density is an intrinsic property of matter, this must be approximately the density of a single molecule.

$$m = DV = (0.9\ g/cm^3)(1.7 \times 10^{-21}\ cm^3) = 1.5 \times 10^{-24}\ kg$$

How good are our assumptions? First, we assumed that the molecules would form a layer one molecule thick. If they didn't, our value for h is only an upper limit on the size of the oleic acid molecule. The assumption that the molecules are cubical in shape is known to be incorrect. The molecule is a long chain that is about 100 atoms long. Furthermore, they tend to line up perpendicular to the surface. This makes the diameter of the chain less than 1 nm.

Obviously, the mass and size of a single hydrogen, carbon, or oxygen atom is much smaller but this experiment gives a simple, though indirect, way of estimating molecular sizes and masses.

7.2 Pressure

The text gives the pressure as a macroscopic property and hints at the microscopic origins of pressure in a gas. Using the concepts of impulse and momentum changes developed in

---

[1] Decreasing the radius of the circle reduces the area by a factor of four, making our estimate of the molecule's height four times bigger.

Chapter 5 and the concept of kinetic energy from Chapter 6, we can get an exact expression that connects the macroscopic, observable pressure with its microscopic origins, namely atomic motion. The derivation is a little messy but has only a few assumptions, and is, thus, relatively straightforward. The derivation can be found in all introductory engineering physics textbooks.

$$P = \frac{2}{3}\frac{N}{V}\left(\frac{1}{2}m\overline{v^2}\right)$$

This says that the pressure is directly proportional to the number of particles N and the average kinetic energy of the particles. It is inversely proportional to the volume V of the container holding the gas.

Example 7.2.1

What is the pressure created in a 1-m^3 box by 1 million molecules of oxygen with an average speed of 500 m/s?

Since the oxygen molecule has two atoms, the mass of the oxygen molecule is 32 amu. The kinetic energy of each oxygen molecule is

$$KE = \frac{1}{2}mv^2 = \frac{1}{2}(32 \times 1.66 \times 10^{-27}\,kg)(500\,m/s)^2 = 6.64 \times 10^{-21}\,J$$

The pressure then becomes

$$P = \frac{2}{3}\frac{N}{V}\left(\frac{1}{2}m\overline{v^2}\right) = \frac{2}{3}\frac{10^6}{1\,m^3}(6.64 \times 10^{-21}\,J) = 4.43 \times 10^{-15}\,\frac{N}{m^2}$$

Notice that this is a very small pressure, only 4.37 x 10^{-20} atm. This occurs because the number of molecules is very small. A box this size would contain about 3 x 10^{25} molecules at atmospheric pressure.

Practice[2]

What happens to the pressure of a gas when the speed of the molecules is doubled?

◆ ◆ ◆

---

[2] Doubling the speed, quadruples the kinetic energy and, therefore, quadruples the pressure.

7.3 Measuring Temperature

To convert from a Fahrenheit temperature to a Celsius temperature we have to subtract 32 degrees from the Fahrenheit reading to get to the zero point on the Celsius scale and then adjust for the different size degrees. Since there are 180° Fahrenheit and 100° Celsius between the freezing point and the boiling point of water, we can calculate the relative sizes of the two degrees.

$$\frac{100^\circ C}{180^\circ F} = \frac{5^\circ C}{9^\circ F}$$

Therefore, the equation for converting $^\circ F$ to $^\circ C$ is

$$T_C = \frac{5^\circ C}{9^\circ F}(T_F - 32^\circ F)$$

where T_C and T_F are the corresponding temperatures in Celsius and Fahrenheit. When writing this equation, it helps to remember that the conversion factor has to have $^\circ F$ in the denominator to cancel the $^\circ F$ in the parentheses. To decide whether to subtract or add the $32^\circ F$, remember that the freezing point of water is $0^\circ C = 32^\circ F$.
    Converting from $^\circ C$ to $^\circ F$ is the reverse of this.

$$T_F = \frac{9^\circ F}{5^\circ C} T_C + 32^\circ F$$

Example 7.3.1.
    What is the temperature in Celsius when your Fahrenheit thermometer reads 100°?

$$T_C = \frac{5^\circ C}{9^\circ F}(T_F - 32^\circ F) = \frac{5^\circ C}{9}(100 - 32) = 37.8^\circ C$$

Practice[3]

    What is the Celsius temperature if your thermometer reads one-half this value, or $50^\circ F$?

Example 7.3.2.
    A European friend writes to you that last summer the temperature in his city reached a high of $40^\circ C$. What is this temperature in Fahrenheit?

---

[3] $10^\circ C$

$$T_F = \frac{9\,°F}{5\,°C}\, T_C + 32\,°F = \frac{9\,°F}{5}\, 40 + 32\,°F = 104\,°F$$

Practice[4]

Room temperature is 20°C. What is it in Fahrenheit?

♦ ♦ ♦

7.4 Absolute Temperature Scale

The conversion from the Celsius temperature scale to the absolute temperature scale is easy because the degrees are the same size, that is, 1°C = 1 K. You just need to add or subtract 273°. If you are converting a Celsius reading to an absolute (or Kelvin) reading, you add the 273°. To convert from Fahrenheit, you must first convert to Celsius.

Example 7.4.1

Oxygen boils at 90 K. What is this temperature in Celsius?

$$T_C = T_K - 273\,°C = 90\,K - 273\,°C = -183\,°C$$

Practice[5]

Room temperature is about 20°C. What is this temperature on the absolute scale?

♦ ♦ ♦

7.5 The Ideal Gas Law: A Microscopic View

In Section 7.2, we connected the pressure as a macroscopic property to the average kinetic energy of the microscopic particles. We can go one step further and look at the origins of temperature. If we multiply both sides of the pressure relationship by the volume of the gas, we get

$$PV = \frac{2}{3} N \left(\frac{1}{2} m \overline{v^2} \right)$$

In computing the average kinetic energy, we square the velocity and then compute the average.

---

[4] 68°F

[5] 293 K

The text states that the ideal gas law is given by

$$PV = cT$$

where the temperature T must be in kelvin.

Comparing these two equations shows that the macroscopic property we call temperature is directly proportional to the average kinetic energy of the atomic or molecular particles.

$$T \propto \frac{1}{2} m \overline{v^2}$$

Therefore, if two gases are at the same temperature, their molecules have equal kinetic energies. This allows us to calculate the ratio of their average speeds. What we actually calculate is a special speed known as the *root mean square* (rms) speed. We calculate the speed squared, take the average, and then take the square root.

$$\frac{1}{2} m_1 \overline{v_1^2} = \frac{1}{2} m_2 \overline{v_2^2}$$

$$\frac{v_1}{v_2} = \sqrt{\frac{m_2}{m_1}}$$

Example 7.5.1

How does the rms speed of hydrogen molecules compare to the rms speed of oxygen molecules in a mixture of the two gases?

In a mixture the two gases are at the same temperature. Thus, we can use our relationship.

$$\frac{v_h}{v_o} = \sqrt{\frac{m_o}{m_j}} = \sqrt{\frac{32 \, amu}{2 \, amu}} = 4$$

Therefore, the hydrogen molecules have 4 times the rms speed of the oxygen molecules.

◆ ◆ ◆

7.6 The Ideal Gas Law: A Macroscopic View

The ideal gas law can be rewritten to show that if we keep the amount and type of gas fixed, the ratio PV/T has a constant value.

$$\frac{PV}{T} = c$$

This means that the three macroscopic quantities - pressure, volume, and temperature - are not independent quantities. We can obtain any one of them if we know the values of the other two.

Since PV/T is a constant and using the subscripts i and f for the initial and final values, we must have

$$\frac{P_f V_f}{T_f} = \frac{P_i V_i}{T_i}$$

Whenever any one of the quantities is held fixed, it can be canceled and we get a relationship between the other two. This gives us the various gas laws stated on page 157 of the text.

Example 7.6.1

What happens to the volume of 50 cm^3 of gas if its temperature is raised from 20°C to 100°C? Assume that the pressure remains the same.

Canceling the pressure, solving for the final volume, and expressing the temperatures in kelvin, we have

$$V_f = V_i \left(\frac{T_f}{T_i} \right) = 50 \ cm^3 \left(\frac{373 \ K}{293 \ K} \right) = 63.7 \ cm^3$$

Notice that any units can be used for the volume. The answer will have the same units as that of the initial volume.

Practice[6]

What is the volume if the temperature is raised another 80°C?

Example 7.6.2

Suppose we have a gas in a cylinder with a movable piston. We measure its pressure, volume, and temperature at the beginning of an experiment. We heat the gas to a new temperature that is three times the original temperature (measured in kelvin). If the volume increases to twice the original volume, what is the new pressure?

---

[6] 77.3 cm^3

$$P_f = P_i \left(\frac{V_i}{V_f}\right)\left(\frac{T_f}{T_i}\right) = P_i \left(\frac{V_i}{2V_i}\right)\left(\frac{3T_i}{T_i}\right) = \frac{3}{2} P_i$$

The final pressure will be 3/2 times the initial pressure.

Practice[7]

What would the new pressure be in the above example if the volume is held fixed during the heating process?

Problems

1. An artist uses 1000 cm^3 of paint (about a quart) to uniformly cover a canvas with an area of 10 m^2. How thick is the average coating of the paint?

2. If a painter uses 40 liters (1000 cm^3 each) to paint a house with a surface area of 300 m^2, what is the thickness of the paint?

3. One liter (1000 cm^3) of Middle Eastern oil is dumped into the Persian Gulf. Assuming that this will spread out evenly over the water to a thickness of 10^{-4} cm, how big an area will the oil cover? How does this compare to the size of a football field?

4. How much paint is required to cover a 500-m^2 barn to a thickness of 0.01 mm?

5. If an atom has a diameter of 0.2 nm, how many of them would it take to form a layer one atom thick on a plate that has an area of 5 cm^2?

6. A cube of gold 1 cm on a side has a mass of 19.3 g and contains 5.9 x 10^{22} atoms. What is the mass of each gold atom?

7. If 6 x 10^{22} nitrogen molecules with an rms speed of 450 m/s occupy a volume of 2 x 10^3 cm^3, what is the pressure? Nitrogen molecules have a mass of 28 amu.

8. Carbon dioxide has a mass of 44 amu. If 10^{22} carbon dioxide molecules have an average speed of 400 m/s and occupy a container with a volume of 500 cm^3, what is the pressure of the gas?

*9. Hydrogen molecules have a mass of 2 amu. If the average speed of the hydrogen molecules is 1600 m/s, how many hydrogen molecules per liter would you need to have a pressure of 1 atm?

*10. If chlorine molecules have a mass of 71 amu and an average speed of 300 m/s, how many chlorine molecules per liter would be required for a pressure of 1 atm?

11. Convert each of these Fahrenheit temperatures to the Celsius scale: -40°F, 0°F and 70°F.

---

[7] The final pressure will be 3 times the initial pressure.

12. The record high temperature on earth is 136°F. What is this temperature on the Celsius scale.

13. Convert each of these Celsius temperatures to the Fahrenheit scale: -40°C, 32°C, and 70°C.

14. The record low temperature on earth is -88°C. What is this temperature on the Fahrenheit scale?

*15. A student decides to devise a new temperature scale with the freezing and boiling points of water at 0°X and 50°X. What Celsius and Fahrenheit temperatures correspond to a temperature of 30°X?

*16. The freezing and boiling points of water on the Rankine temperature scale are 492°R and 672°R, respectively. What is normal body temperature on this scale?

17. Convert each of the following temperatures to the Kelvin scale: -40°F and 37°C.

18. Liquid nitrogen has a boiling point of -196°C. What is this temperature on the Kelvin and Fahrenheit scales?

19. Convert each of the following temperatures to the Celsius scale: 0 K and 310 K.

20. The melting point of gold is 1337 K. What is the melting point on the Celsius and Fahrenheit scales?

*21. The mass of an oxygen molecule is 16 times that of a hydrogen molecule. How do the average speeds of these molecules compare if the gases are at the same temperature?

*22. The mass of a nitrogen molecule is 0.88 times that of an oxygen molecule. If the average speed of a nitrogen molecule is 511 m/s at 20°C, what is the average speed on an oxygen molecule at this temperature?

23. What happens to the temperature of an ideal gas if you reduce its volume to one-third while holding the pressure constant?

24. If you hold the temperature of an ideal gas constant, what happens to its volume when you triple its pressure?

25. Two liters of gas at 20°C is heated to 100°C while the pressure is maintained at 1 atm. What is the final volume of the gas?

26. Three liters of gas at 20°C and 1 atm in a container with a fixed volume is cooled to -20°C. What is the final pressure of the gas?

27. A volume of 150 cm^3 of an ideal gas has an initial temperature of 20°C and an initial pressure of 1 atm. What is the final pressure if the volume is reduced to 100 cm^3 and the temperature is raised to 40°C?

28. An ideal gas has the following initial conditions: V_i = 500 cm^3, P_i = 3 atm, and T_i =100°C. What is its final temperature if the pressure is reduced to 1 atm and the volume expands to 1000 cm^3?

29. A tank of helium has a volume of 4 liters and a pressure of 80 atm. How many balloons can it fill if each balloon has volume of 1 liter and requires a pressure of 1 atm?

*30. A 0.2 m^3 tank of helium has a pressure of 100 atm. Each balloon requires a pressure of 1.25 atm (0.25 atm above the pressure in the room) and has a volume of 5,000 cm^3. How many balloons can be filled from the tank?

8 STATES OF MATTER

8.1 Density

Density is an important, fundamental property of matter because it is an *intrinsic* property. This means that density doesn't change with a change in the amount of material or the shape of the object. A gold wedding ring has the same density as a pound of gold. And the pound of gold could have a cubical, spherical, or any other shape. However, the object cannot be hollow. The density of a hollow object is just the average density of the material and the air inside. Composite materials have a range of densities depending on the relative amounts of the different substances.

The units of density in the SI system are kg/m^3. However, the units of g/cm^3 are also widely used. Convince yourself that you can convert to g/cm^3 by dividing the density in kg/m^3 by 1000. Therefore, the density of water is $1000 \ kg/m^3 = 1 \ g/cm^3$. The densities of some common substances are given in Table 8-1 of the text on page 166.

Example 8.1.1

What is the average density of the sun?

The mass and radius of the sun are given in the tables in the Appendix of this manual. Since the sun is very nearly spherical, we can calculate its volume V_s to be

$$V_s = \frac{4}{3}\pi r^3 = (4.19)(6.96 \times 10^8 \ m)^3 = 1.41 \times 10^{27} \ m^3$$

The sun's density is therefore

$$D_s = \frac{M_s}{V_s} = \frac{1.99 \times 10^{30} \ kg}{1.41 \times 10^{27} \ m^3} = 1410 \ kg/m^3$$

Therefore, the average density of the sun is 1.4 times that of water. This figure is an average density for the sun. The density varies from a high of 150 g/cm^3 at its center to a low of $2.3 \times 10^{-8} \ g/cm^3$ at its visible surface. The average density of the earth is 5.5 g/cm^3.

Practice[1]

If the mass of the sun was compressed to a volume equal to that of earth, what would be the new density of this compact sun?

---

[1] $1.84 \times 10^9 \ kg/m^3$

8.2 Elasticity

When a force tries to compress or stretch many materials, the change in their size is too small to observe directly. Rubber bands, silly putty, and springs are obvious exceptions to this. If a rubber band or spring is stretched, it will return to its original shape provided the stretch is not too large. Under these conditions, the object obeys Hooke's law

$$F = kx$$

where F is the net force on the spring or rubber band and x is the displacement, or the change in length, and k is the *spring constant*. The spring constant tells us how much force is required to stretch (or compress) the spring a unit length. In the SI system of units, the spring constant is usually expressed in N/m.

Example 8.2.1

A bathroom scale, which is spring loaded, is compressed 3 cm when an 80-kg person stands on it. What's the spring constant for this bathroom scale?

$$k = \frac{F}{x} = \frac{mg}{x} = \frac{(80\,kg)(9.81\,m/s^2)}{0.03\,m} = 26{,}200\,N/m$$

Practice[2]

A bathroom scale is being designed by an engineering student. She wants the scale's spring to compress only 3 cm when a 115-kg person stands on it. What spring constant is needed?

◆ ◆ ◆

8.3 Atmospheric Pressure

In the Section in the text entitled *Pressure* we said that pressure increases as one goes deeper into a liquid. We justified this statement by showing that the pressure at that level must be large enough to support a column of liquid above this level (Fig. 8-13). As one goes deeper, the column gets longer and the pressure required to support the weight of the column must increase. The upward force is the product of the pressure P and the cross-sectional area A of the column. The weight W of the column is Mg where M is its mass. Equating these two expressions, we have

$$PA = W = Mg$$

---

[2] 37,600 N/m

The mass can be obtained from the density D and the volume V of the liquid.

$$M = DV = DAh$$

where h is the height of the column, or the depth of the level. Substituting this expression for the mass into our equation for the pressure and canceling the areas, we obtain the relationship for pressure.

$$P = Dgh$$

This relationship holds for the atmosphere, but it is more complicated because the density varies with altitude and the top of the atmosphere is hard to determine. Solids and liquids are easier because they are nearly incompressible, making density variations with depth negligible.

The atmospheric pressure at a particular level can be measured with a barometer (Fig. 8-16). The atmospheric pressure is equal to the pressure at the bottom of the mercury column because the weight of the mercury column is supported by the air pressure.

Example 8.3.1

What is the height of a mercury column if the air pressure is equal to 1 atm? The density of mercury is 13,600 kg/m^3.

$$h = \frac{P}{Dg} = \frac{1.01 \times 10^5 \, N/m^2}{(13{,}600 \, kg/m^3)(9.81 \, m/s^2)} = 0.757 \, m$$

Example 8.3.2

If you made a barometer with water instead of mercury, how high would the column of water reach?

Both the pressure due to the water column and the pressure due to the mercury column are equal to the atmospheric pressure, so we can set them equal to each other.

$$D_w g h_w = D_m g h_m$$

where the subscripts w and m refer to water and mercury. Canceling the common factor g and solving for the height of the water column, we have

$$h_w = h_m \left(\frac{D_m}{D_w} \right) = 0.757 \, m \left(\frac{13.6 \, g/cm^3}{1 \, g/cm^3} \right) = 10.3 \, m$$

Since mercury is 13.6 times more dense than water, the height of the water column is 13.6 times taller than the mercury column for all values of atmospheric pressure.

Practice[3]

Suppose you made a barometer of oil that has a density of 900 kg/m^3. How high would the oil column be when the mercury column is 76 cm tall?

◆ ◆ ◆

8.4 Sink and Float

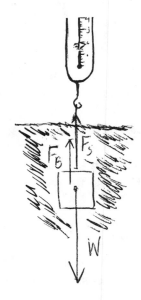

Archimedes' principle states that an object in a fluid (either a liquid or a gas) is buoyed up by a force equal to the weight of the volume of fluid displaced. If the object is suspended from a string while it is completely submerged as shown in Fig. 8.4.1, this buoyant force F_b reduces the force needed to support the object. The force F_s of the string is known as the weight of the object in the fluid and can be calculated from

$$F_s = W - F_b = D_o V_o g - D_f V_o g = (D_o - D_f)V_o g$$

where V_o is the volume of the object, g is the acceleration due to gravity, and D_o and D_f are the densities of the object and fluid, respectively. How would this equation change if the object were less dense than the fluid and anchored to the bottom by the string?

Fig. 8.4.1

Example 8.4.1

A sphere of aluminum has a volume of 0.01 m^3 and a density of 2700 kg/m^3. What is the weight of the sphere when it is under water?

$$F_s = (D_o - D_f)V_o g$$

$$= (2700\ kg/m^3 - 1000\ kg/m^3)(0.01\ m^3)(9.81\ m/s^2) = 167\ N$$

compared with a weight of 265 N in air.

◆ ◆ ◆

How deep something sinks into water depends on its density. Suppose that we have a piece of clay about the size of a golf ball. Since the density of clay is greater than that of water, we know that an equal volume of water will weigh less than the clay. Thus, the clay will sink, as we expect. We can make this ball a clay a "floater" if we mold it into the shape of a

---

[3] 11.5 m

small bowl. When we set it onto the water's surface, it starts to sink, displacing water. It continues to sink until it has displaced a volume of water that weighs the same as the clay. Under this condition

$$D_o V_o = D_f V_f$$

where V_f is the volume of the water displaced. If the sides are too short, water flows over the sides before this can occur and the clay sinks.

Example 8.4.2

How far down will a plastic cup sink in water? Assume that the cup is a cylinder with a cross-sectional area of 6 cm^2, that it has a mass of 30 g, and that it remains vertical.

The cup will sink until it has displaced 30 g of water. Since the density of water is 1 g/cm^3, it will sink until it displaces 30 cm^3 of water.

$$h = \frac{V}{A} = \frac{30\ cm^3}{6\ cm^2} = 5\ cm$$

Practice[4]

If a 10 g mass is placed in the cup, how much farther will the cup sink?

◆ ◆ ◆

Problems

1. What is the density of gasoline if a liter has a mass of 0.68 kg?
2. What is the density of cottonseed oil if one liter has a mass of 926 g?
3. What is the average density of Mars? How does this compare with the average density of earth?
4. A neutron star has about 1.2 times the mass of the sun and a volume about equal to the volume of the earth. What is the average density of a neutron star?

5. If you have a solid cube of aluminum that you measure to be 2 cm on each edge, how much mass will you have?
6. You have a solid ring that you suspect is pure gold. If you measure the ring to have a volume of 0.06 cm^3, what should the ring's mass be?
7. What volume does 0.5 kg of mercury occupy?
8. What is the volume of a lead weight that has a mass of 16 g?

---

[4] An additional 1.67 cm

9. A 1-kg mass stretches a spring 6 cm. What is the spring constant in N/m?

10. If a 15-kg mass compresses a scale 0.6 m, what is the spring constant in N/m?

11. A spring has a spring constant of 40 N/m. If a 1.5-kg mass is hung from it, how far will it stretch?

12. How far will a spring with a spring constant of 50 N/m stretch if a 3 kg mass is hung from it?

13. What mass is required to compress a spring 2 cm if the spring constant is 500 N/m?

*14. Two springs with spring constant k are hanging side by side. If a mass is hung from both of them, what is the effective spring constant of the pair?

15. A scuba diver is 15 m below the surface of a lake. What is the pressure on her body just due to the water?

16. What is the pressure at a depth of 1 km under water? Is the atmospheric pressure important?

17. How deep must one go in water to reach a pressure of 5 atm?

18. How deep must one go in a tank of mercury to reach a pressure of 5 atm?

19. A submarine dives to a depth of 100 m. What is the pressure on its surface if the density of seawater is 1.03 g/cm^3?

20. Each cubic inch of water has a weight of 0.036 lb. What is the pressure at the bottom of a column of water 10 ft tall if there is a vacuum above the water?

21. A dam holds a lake back that has a surface area of 10 km^2 and a depth of 12 m. What is the water pressure at the base of the dam?

22. What is the pressure at the base of a gasoline storage tank that is 12 m in diameter and 8 m tall? The density of gasoline is 0.68 g/cm^3.

23. A block of metal has a mass of 2.3 kg and a volume of 0.001 m^3. What is the weight of the block under water?

24. What is the weight of 1 kg of gold under water?

25. A piece of metal weighs 0.9 N in air and 0.7 N when submerged in water. What is its volume?

26. A piece of wood weighs 20 N. When placed in water, it just barely floats. What is its volume?

27. A block of aluminum has a mass of 2.7 kg. If it were reshaped into a boat, how much volume would it need to displace in order to float?

28. What is the volume displaced by a 500,000-(metric) ton freighter?

29. A hollow block of aluminum is floating in water. If it has a mass of 27 kg and a volume of 0.1 m^3, how much of it will be above the surface?

30. A sphere has a mass of 365 g and a volume of 635 cm^3. What fraction of the sphere will float above the surface of the water?

9 THERMAL ENERGY

9.1 Mechanical Work and Heat

It takes a lot of mechanical work to raise the temperature of something. This is good. If the opposite were true, scuffing our feet on the floor could end up cooking our feet. In Chapter 6 we learned that the work done on an object is equal to the net force multiplied by the distance through which the force is applied (the force has to be in the direction of the displacement). Therefore, the frictional force associated with scuffing our feet acting through the lengths of the scuffs does mechanical work which is equivalent to heating the object.

Example 9.1.1

Imagine that you are sitting in a bathtub with 20 liters of water and that the water is too cool (40°C). You decide to heat the water by moving your arms back and forth through the water. Under the very unrealistic assumption that there is no heat loss, how long would it take to raise the temperature of the water 1°C?

Let's assume that you move your arms back and forth once every 2 s, each swing is 1-m long, and the average force F exerted is 20 N in each direction. Therefore, the amount of mechanical work W performed each second is the force times the distance d moved.

$$W = Fd = (20\,N)(1\,m) = 20\,J$$

Since this is the energy per second, the power P is 20 W.

To calculate the amount of heat needed to raise the temperature of the water, we need to know the mass m of the water.

$$m = DV = (1\,g/cm^3)(20\,L)\left(\frac{1000\,cm^3}{1\,L}\right) = 2 \times 10^4\,g$$

Since it takes 1 cal to raise the temperature of 1 g of water by 1°C, the amount of heat Q required to raise the temperature of this water by 1°C is 2×10^4 cal.

Dividing the total amount of thermal energy required by the rate of generating mechanical energy yields the time required. However, we must remember to convert one of the energy units to the other.

$$t = \frac{E}{P} = \frac{2 \times 10^4\,cal}{20\,J/s}\left(\frac{4.19\,J}{1\,cal}\right) = 4190\,s = 69.8\,min$$

Practice[1]

> How would the time required change if you decided to push twice as hard?

◆ ◆ ◆

9.2 Specific Heat

Toward the end of this section in the text we talk about bringing two objects into thermal contact with each other. If this is done in a perfectly insulated environment or if the time we are considering is very short, we can assume that there is no flow of energy out of the system. This means that the energy lost by the hot object is equal to the energy gained by the cold object. However, the temperature changes of the objects are not necessarily the same.

Example 9.2.1

> Consider a 25-g aluminum cube at a temperature of $T_a = 60°C$. If this cube is placed in 100 g of room-temperature water ($T_w = 20°C$), what is the final temperature of the system?
>
> We set the heat lost by the aluminum equal to the heat gained by the water. The specific heats for water c_w and aluminum c_a are 1 cal/g·°C and 0.215 cal/g·°C, respectively.
>
> $$m_w c_w (T_f - T_w) = m_a c_a (T_a - T_f)$$
>
> Solving for the final temperature, we get
>
> $$T_f = \frac{m_w c_w T_w + m_a c_a T_a}{m_w c_w + m_a c_a}$$
>
> $$= \frac{(100\,g)(1\,cal/g·°C)(20°C) + (25\,g)(0.215\,cal/g·°C)(60°C)}{(100\,g)(1\,cal/g·°C) + (25\,g)(0.215\,cal/g·°C)} = 22°C$$

Practice[2]

> If the cube were made of copper ($c_c = 0.093$ cal/g·C), what would the final temperature be?

---

[1] It would take one-half as long.

[2] 20.9°C

9.3 Change of State

The latent heat for a substance is the amount of energy required to change the physical state of a unit mass. For example, when water changes from a solid (ice) to a liquid, 80 cal/g (334 kJ/kg) are required to break the bonds in the ice. The values for the latent heat given in Table 9-2 in the text show that the values vary over a large range. In the reverse process the same amount of energy is given off. Therefore, this table also gives the latent heats of solidification and condensation.

Example 9.3.1

A 20-kg block of ice at 0°C melts to form a puddle of water at 0°C. How much energy is absorbed by the ice?

The latent heat of melting for water is 334 kJ/kg, so the energy needed to change the physical state of the block from ice to liquid water is

$$Q = m_w L_w = (20\,kg)(334\,kJ/kg) = 6680\,kJ$$

Although the puddle is still at the same temperature, it has more energy. The energy went into breaking the molecular bonds.

Practice[3]

If there was half as much ice, how much energy would be absorbed?

Example 9.3.2

If the process is reversed, that is, the puddle at 0°C is frozen, how much energy will be given off by the water?

The same amount of energy will be given off. This is very much like a spring that has been stretched, and at some later time will be released. The energy is stored in the spring and then released.

◆ ◆ ◆

9.4 Conduction

Heat is conducted in a material through exchanges of kinetic energy between its molecules. Conduction occurs when there are temperature differences in the material. The rate Q/t at

---

[3] 3340 kJ

which heat passes through a slab of material depends on the temperature difference ΔT between the two sides, the thermal conductivity k of the material, and the area A and thickness L of the slab. This can be written as

$$\frac{Q}{t} = k\frac{A\,\Delta T}{L}$$

Example 9.4.1

An iron plate is 2 cm thick with a cross-sectional area of 300 cm^2. One face is held at 150°C and the other is 10°C colder. How much heat passes through the plate each second? Assume that the thermal conductivity for iron is 80 W/m·K.

$$\frac{Q}{t} = k\frac{A\,\Delta T}{L} = \left(80\,\frac{W}{m{\cdot}K}\right)\frac{(300\,cm^2)(10\,^oC)}{2\,cm}\left(\frac{1\,m}{100\,cm}\right) = 1200\,W$$

Practice[4]

What happens to the rate if two plates are placed face to face?

◆ ◆ ◆

9.5 Radiation

All objects emit and absorb electromagnetic radiation. The rate P at which an object emits radiation depends on its area A and its absolute temperature T as given by the Stefan-Boltzmann law.

$$P = e\sigma AT^4$$

where e is the emissivity and σ is Stefan's constant, which has the value $\sigma = 5.67 \times 10^{-8}$ W/m^2·K^4 for all substances. The emissivity ranges in value from 0 to 1 and depends on the surface characteristics of the object. An emissivity of 1 means that the object is a perfect absorber of radiation; all of the radiation incident on the object is absorbed. An emissivity of 0 means that the object is a perfect reflector of radiation; none of the radiation is absorbed.

The rate at which an object absorbs radiation is given by the same formula with the temperature T_o of the surroundings substituted for T. Therefore, the net power radiated by the object is given by

---

[4] The rate is cut in half.

$$P = e\sigma A(T^4 - T_o^4)$$

If the object is warmer than the surroundings, the object will have a net energy loss and its temperature will drop. If the surroundings are warmer, the object will have a net gain and its temperature will rise. This difference between the rates of emission and absorption will exist until an equilibrium is reached. This is the reason a room can feel cold even after the furnace has warmed the air. The walls are still colder than the air and there is a net flow of radiation to the walls.

Example 9.5.1

What is the net rate at which a naked person radiates energy in a room at 20°C?

Let's assume that the person approximates a perfect emitter (and absorber) with an emissivity $e = 1$ and has a surface area of 1.5 m². Skin temperature is usually a few degrees below body temperature of 37°C, so let's assume a skin temperature of 33°C = 306 K.

$$P = e\sigma A(T^4 - T_o^4)$$
$$= (1)\left(5.67 \times 10^{-8}\ \frac{W}{m^2 K^4}\right)(1.5\ m^2)[(306\ K)^4 - (293\ K)^4] = 119\ W$$

This is a large power loss, a little more than a 100-W light bulb. At this rate, a person would need to consume about 200 Calories each hour to make up for this loss. Remember that calories with a capital C means food calories, or kcal.

♦ ♦ ♦

The electromagnetic radiation emitted and absorbed by all objects has a range of frequencies and wavelengths. The distribution of wavelengths -- the intensity of the radiation in each wavelength region -- depends on the object's temperature. The distribution drops to zero at high and low wavelengths and has a characteristic hump at intermediate wavelengths as shown in Fig. 22-15 in the text. The wavelength λ_{max} corresponding to the peak intensity is given by Wien's law.

$$\lambda_{max} = \frac{2.9 \times 10^6\ nm \cdot K}{T}$$

where the temperature T must be expressed in kelvin.

Example 9.5.2

What is the peak wavelength radiated from your skin?

$$\lambda_{max} = \frac{2.9 \times 10^6 \, nm \cdot K}{T} = \frac{2.9 \times 10^6 \, nm \cdot K}{306 \, K} = 9480 \, nm$$

According to Fig. 21-26 in the text, this wavelength lies around the middle of the infrared region, an invisible part of the electromagnetic spectrum. If we were to shut off all the lights in a room, you would not be visible with human eyes. Infrared sensing devices, however, would "see" you.

Practice[5]

What is the peak wavelength of a stove element at a temperature of 800°C?

♦ ♦ ♦

9.6 Thermal Expansion

We argued in the text that the thermal expansion ΔL in the length of an object depended on the original length L, the change in temperature ΔT, and the coefficient of thermal expansion α which is characteristic of the material.

$$\Delta L = \alpha \, L \, \Delta T$$

Example 9.6.1

If an aluminum bar has a length of 10.0000 m at a temperature of 20°C and a length of 10.0096 m at 60°C, what is the coefficient of thermal expansion of aluminum?

Solving our equation for α, we have

$$\alpha = \frac{\Delta L}{L \, \Delta T} = \frac{0.0096 \, m}{(10.0000 \, m)(40 \, ^oC)} = 2.4 \times 10^{-5} / ^oC$$

♦ ♦ ♦

---

[5] 2700 nm. Although this peak wavelength is still in the infrared, we can see the element glow red because the wavelength distribution has enough contribution to the visible region of 400-750 nm.

9 Thermal Energy

Problems

1. While a system is being cooled, 8 J of heat are removed and 20 J of work are done on it. What is the change in the internal energy of the system?

2. If it requires 400 J of work to compress an ideal gas and its internal energy increases by 150 J, how much heat is released?

3. If it requires a force of 500 N to push a box across a warehouse floor a distance of 10 m, how many calories of thermal energy are generated?

4. A 1-kg book falls from a table that is 70 cm high. How many calories of thermal energy are produced?

5. It is often said that a person gives off heat equivalent to a 75-W light bulb. How many Cal/s is this?

*6. In a laboratory exercise to verify Joule's result for the mechanical equivalent of heat, a student observed that when a 45-kg mass dropped a distance of 2 m, the temperature of 1000 g of water rose by 0.2°C. How many joules are equivalent to one calorie? How might you account for the difference in this result and the one given in the chapter?

7. How many Cal/s would need to be consumed to equal the power of a 1000-W hair dryer?

8. A typical daily allowance of food energy is about 2500 kcal. How long would you have to exercise at the rate of 4 kJ/min to completely "burn off" a day's consumption?

9. How much heat is released when 500 g of water are cooled from 20°C to 0°C?

10. How much heat is needed to raise the temperature of 800 g of water by 5°C?

11. Assume that you measure the heat required to change the temperature of a fixed mass of water by 5°C. What temperature change will occur if you supply the same amount of heat to an equal mass of gold?

12. How much heat is require to change the temperature of 1 kg of lead by 15°C?

13. The temperature of an unknown metal increases by 10°C when 43 cal of heat are added. If the mass of the metal is determined to be 20 g, identify the metal from the data in Table 9-1.

14. What is the specific heat of a metal that requires 300 cal to change the temperature of a 120-g sample by 12°C?

15. An unknown amount of water at 100°C is mixed with 200 g of water at 50°C in a completely insulated container. If the final equilibrium temperature of the mixture is 80°C, what is the mass of the hot water?

*16. One hundred grams of gold at 70°C is placed into a completely insulated container containing an equal mass of water at 30°C. If the container is made of aluminum and has a mass of 10 g, calculate the final temperature of the gold-water-aluminum system.

17. Forty grams of gold at a temperature of 100°C are placed in 100 g of water at 19°C. What is the equilibrium temperature if no energy is lost to the surroundings?

18. What is the equilibrium temperature if a 50-g sample of aluminum at 90°C is placed in 150 g of water at 18°C?

19. When a sample of copper at 96°C is placed into 200 g of water at 20°C, the equilibrium temperature is 22°C. What is the mass of the sample?

*20. Given that 1 lb. of water has a mass of 454 g, show that 1 BTU is equal to 252 cal.

21. How much heat is released when 400 g of water at 0°C freezes?

22. How much heat is required to convert 400 g of water at 100°C to steam at 100°C?

23. How does the amount of heat required to convert 1 g of water at 100°C to steam at 100°C compare to the amount of thermal energy required to heat 1 g of water from 20°C to 100°C? (This is why some radiators use steam rather than hot water.)

24. How much heat is required to convert 400 g of ice at -5°C to water at +5°C?

*25. What is the maximum mass of 100°C water that can be cooled to 0°C with 100 g of ice at 0°C?

*26. A 100-g cube of aluminum at -20°C is put into 300 g of water at 0°C. How much ice will freeze?

27. A concrete wall is 10 cm thick and has a surface area of 5 m³. At what rate will thermal energy pass through the wall if the inside and outside temperatures are 20°C and -10°C?

28. A 1.9-cm thick wood wall with a surface area of 5 m³ has a temperature of 20°C on one side and 0°C on the other. What is the heat loss through the wall per second?

29. If the earth was a perfect radiator (it isn't), it would have a temperature of 400 K. If this were true, how much energy would the earth radiate for each square meter of its surface?

*30. What is the power radiated by the sun assuming that it is a perfect radiator with a temperature of 5800 K?

31. What is the peak wavelength of the radiation emitted from boiling water?

32. What temperature is required for an object to have a peak wavelength in the middle of the visible spectrum?

33. What is the peak wavelength emitted by the sun? Assume that the surface temperature of the sun is 5800 K.

34. Why might a large star with a surface temperature of 3000 K be called a red giant?

35. If telephone wires between poles separated by 40 m are fairly taut at a temperature of -30°C, how much longer will the wire be when the temperature reaches +30°C? Copper has a coefficient of thermal expansion of $1.7 \times 10^{-5}/°C$.

36. If sections of a concrete highway are 20 m long when poured at a temperature of 20°C, how big a space must be left between sections if the concrete could reach temperatures of 50°C? The thermal coefficient of thermal expansion for concrete is $1.2 \times 10^{-5}/°C$.

37. A steel I-beam used in the construction of a building is 12 m long. By how much does its length change between the extreme temperatures of -40°C and +50°C?

38. If steel rails used by the Union Pacific Railroad have a length of 30 m and a gap between rails of 2 mm at 20°C, what size gap will appear at -30°C?

*39. The volume coefficient of thermal expansion is 1.82×10^{-4}/°C for mercury. If the volume of mercury is 1 liter at 20°C, what is its volume at 40°C?

*40. An aluminum plate is 10 cm by 10 cm at 20°C. By how much will its area increase when it is heated to 100°C?

10   AVAILABLE ENERGY

10.1   Real Engines

The maximum efficiency of your automobile's engine can be calculated using Carnot's relationship for an ideal heat engine. The Carnot efficiency η_C is given by

$$\eta_C = 1 - \frac{T_c}{T_h}$$

where T_h and T_c are the absolute temperatures of the hot and cold reservoirs, respectively. To obtain the actual efficiency η, we need to measure the amount of heat put into the engine and the amount of work that it does.

$$\eta = \frac{W}{Q}$$

Example 10.1.1

An engine with a power output of 200 kW operates between temperatures of 500°C and 30°C. If it requires energy at a rate of 6 x 10^5 J/s to operate, what are its Carnot and actual efficiencies?

To find the Carnot efficiency, we need to convert the Celsius temperature to the absolute scale and insert them into the Carnot relationship.

$$\eta_C = 1 - \frac{T_c}{T_h} = 1 - \frac{303\ K}{773\ K} = 60.8\%$$

To calculate the actual efficiency, we look at the input energy and work out during 1 s.

$$\eta = \frac{W}{Q} = \frac{2 \times 10^5\ J}{6 \times 10^5\ J} = 33.3\%$$

Therefore, the losses due to friction and the flow of thermal energy to the surrounds reduces the efficiency by 27.5%.

Practice[1]

What are the efficiencies if the higher temperature increases to 600°C?

---

[1] η_C = 65.3%; η = 33.3% (no change)

Example 10.1.2

Suppose that a gasoline engine has a maximum theoretical efficiency of 30% and you measure the temperature of the exhausted gases to be 30°C. What is the minimum possible temperature inside the cylinders after the combustion?

The minimum temperature is given by the Carnot efficiency.

$$T_h = \frac{T_c}{1 - \eta} = \frac{303 \ K}{0.70} = 433 \ K = 160\,^oC$$

A real engine would require a higher temperature to compensate for the lower efficiency.

Practice[2]

If the efficiency of the engine is increased to 40%, what is the new cylinder temperature?

◆ ◆ ◆

10.2 Running Heat Engines Backward

The "efficiency" of a refrigerator is called the *coefficient of performance* and is equal to the heat Q_c extracted from the cold-temperature region divided by the work W required to make the transfer (See Fig. 10-12 in the text).

$$COP = \frac{Q_c}{W}$$

A good refrigerator extracts a lot of heat from the objects that you want to keep cold with a minimum amount of work. Good refrigerators have COP's of 5 or 6.

If we consider our refrigerator to be a Carnot engine running backward, we can get an expression for the COP in terms of the temperatures T_h and T_c of the hot and cold regions.

$$COP = \frac{T_c}{T_h - T_c}$$

---

[2] 505 K

Example 10.2.1

> If we have a refrigerator with an internal temperature of 0°C and an exhaust temperature 33°C, what is its maximum COP?
>
> By asking for the maximum COP, we are assuming that the refrigerator is a Carnot engine running backward. This means that the efficiency can be expressed as
>
> $$COP = \frac{T_c}{T_h - T_c} = \frac{273\ K}{306\ K - 273\ K} = 8.27$$

Practice[3]

> What will the exhaust temperature be if you lower the thermostat to -10°C and assume that the COP doesn't change?

◆ ◆ ◆

10.3 Entropy

The relationship between the disorder of a system and entropy can be expressed mathematically as discovered by Ludwig Boltzmann. The Boltzmann equation is

$$S = k\ log W$$

where S is the entropy of the system, k is a constant, and W is, loosely speaking, the number of different, but equivalent, ways that a system can be put together. Strictly speaking, this relationship only holds for systems with very large numbers of states. The *log* function means that you keep only the power of ten in W. If the ratio does not yield a whole number for the power of ten, you can still obtain an answer by putting the value of W into a calculator and pushing the "log" button.

Example 10.3.1

> As an artificial, but illustrative example, let's return to the case of our coins. For simplicity assume that the constant k is equal to one. The entropy for the case of all heads (or all tails) would be
>
> $$S = k\ log(1) = 0$$
>
> since $1 = 10^0$. The entropy for the case of two heads and two tails would be

---

[3] 31.8°C

$$S = k \log(4) = 0.602$$

since there are four ways of obtaining two heads and two tails.

In thermodynamics, the system is more disordered when it has a higher number of equivalent states. We see that the Boltzmann relationship shows that the system also has a higher entropy.

Practice[4]

In all situations we are interested in the change in the entropy, not the actual value of the entropy. What would be the effect of putting in the correct value of Boltzmann's constant?

◆ ◆ ◆

Problems

1. An engine with an efficiency of 20% does 100 J of work. How much energy does it take in?

2. If an engine has an output of 200 W and exhausts 100 J of heat each second, what is its efficiency?

3. What is the efficiency of a heat engine that takes in 6 cal of heat and does 8.4 J of mechanical work?

4. A salesperson claims that his best engine will do 12 J of mechanical work for each 3 cal of heat taken in. Is this possible?

5. A modern steam turbine typically has a maximum input temperature of 810 K (999°F) and an outlet temperature of 310 K (98°F). What is its maximum theoretical efficiency?

6. A heat engine takes in 8000 cal of energy at 800 K and exhausts 6000 cal at 400 K. What is the efficiency of this engine? What is its maximum theoretical efficiency?

*7. A typical coal-fired electric power plant has an efficiency of 38%, while a nuclear power plant is more like 32% efficient. How many joules of thermal energy is required by each plant to generate one joule of electrical energy? How much does each plant exhaust as waste? Is the 6% difference in efficiency important?

*8. A steam turbine has an efficiency of 47%. If one now includes a boiler efficiency of 88% and a generator efficiency of 99%, what is the overall efficiency of the electrical generating system? (Hint: 88% of the original energy leaves the boiler, 47% of that leaves the turbine and 99% of that leaves the generator.)

9. A refrigerator uses 4.2 J of electrical energy to remove 1 cal of heat from its internal space. What is its coefficient of performance?

---

[4] The relative changes would be the same, but the size of the change would be scaled by the constant.

10. A refrigerator exhausts 1000 cal of heat from its internal space with a coefficient of performance of 5.6. How much work is performed by the refrigerator?

11. A heat pump (working like a refrigerator) extracts energy from a cold reservoir that is at 5°C and expels it to a hotter reservoir at 15°C. What is its coefficient of performance if you assume that the heat pump is an ideal Carnot engine running backward?

12. An air conditioner moves energy from a room at 20°C and expels it to the outside which is at 30°C. What is its coefficient of performance if you assume that the heat pump is an ideal Carnot engine running backward?

13. Suppose you had a paper bag filled with 50 colored marbles. Ten of the marbles are red and the remainder are white. What is the probability of reaching in and pulling out a red marble?

14. Suppose you have removed a red marble in the previous problem. What is the probability of reaching in and pulling out a second red marble?

15. Poker chips have two colors; red on one side and blue on the other. If you put four in a bag, shake the bag, and dump them on a table, how many different ways can you have exactly two chips with the red side up?

16. How many different ways can you throw a total of 7 with 3 dice? What is the probability of getting a total of 7 on a single throw?

*17. Imagine that you have dice with 12 faces that are all the same so that the likelihood of any one face being on top is the same as any other face. If the faces are numbered 1 through 12, what is the probability of rolling a total of 13 with two such dice?

*18. Suppose you had a paper bag filled with 50 colored marbles. Ten of the marbles are red and the remainder are white. What is the probability of reaching in and pulling out a red marble?

19. Find the entropy of 100 pennies with all the heads up. There are 1×10^{29} possible arrangement for half heads and half tails. What is the maximum possible change in entropy?

*20. Find the entropy of three identical coins for the different arrangements assuming that k = 1. What is the maximum possible change in entropy?

11   IS IT ALL RELATIVE?

11.1 Comparing Velocities

In the text we described a situation in which your friends were rolling a ball on the floor of a moving truck. We stated that the velocity of the ball measured relative to the ground was equal to the *vector* sum of the velocity of the truck measured relative to the ground and the velocity of the ball measured relative to the truck. We can translate these words into a vector equation.

$$v_{og} = v_{os} + v_{sg}$$

where the subscripts o, g, and s refer to the object, ground, and moving reference system, respectively. Therefore, v_{og} is the velocity of the object (the ball) measured relative to the ground, v_{os} is the velocity of the object measured relative to the moving reference system (the truck), and v_{sg} is the velocity of the system measured relative to the ground. The key to finding velocities using this vector relationship is to carefully identify the meaning of each symbol and to not forget their vector properties. In motion along a straight line, we can once again use plus and minus signs to denote the directions of the velocities.

Example 11.1.1

Let's rework the example in the text. The ball rolled on the floor at 2 m/s toward the east. The truck was traveling at 3 m/s toward the east. What is the velocity of the ball measured relative to the ground?

Choosing east as the positive direction and identifying the ball as the object and the truck as the moving reference system, we have

$$v_{og} = v_{sg} + v_{os} = +2\,m/s + 3\,m/s = 5\,m/s$$

Therefore, the ball is moving 5 m/s eastward relative to the ground. If the ball were rolled toward the back of the truck, we would have

$$v_{og} = v_{sg} + v_{os} = -2\,m/s + 3\,m/s = 1\,m/s$$

In this case the ball is still moving toward the east (indicated by the plus sign) but its speed relative to the ground has been reduced to 1 m/s.

Practice[1]

What is the speed of the ball relative to the ground if it is rolled toward the back of the truck at 4 m/s?

------

[1] -1 m/s or 1 m/s westward

Example 11.1.2

What would the ball's speed be relative to the ground in Example 11.1.1 if it were rolled directly to the side of the truck?

We can draw a vector diagram like that in Fig. 11.1.1 and measure the size of the resultant vector. Alternatively, since the two velocity vectors are perpendicular to each other, we can also obtain the speed using the Pythagorean theorem.

$$v_{og} = \sqrt{v_{os}^2 + v_{sg}^2} = \sqrt{(2\ m/s)^2 + (3\ m/s)^2} = \sqrt{13}\ m/s = 3.61\ m/s$$

The direction θ of the velocity of the ball relative to the ground can be measured on the diagram to be $34°$.

◆ ◆ ◆

11.2 Realistic Inertial Forces

Let's use the elevator described in the text as our example situation for solving problems involving accelerating reference systems. If the acceleration of the elevator is *a* and the mass of the person standing on the scales is *m*, Newton's second law tells us that

$$F_{net} = F_s + F_g = ma$$

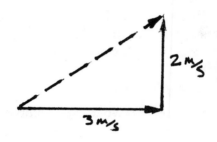

Fig. 11.1.1

where $F_g = mg$, the force of gravity acting on the person, and F_s is the force exerted by the scales on the person. We must be careful of the vector nature of this relationship when we apply it to specific situations.

Example 11.2.1

A 90-kg person is standing on bathroom scales in an elevator that has an acceleration of 2 m/s^2 upward. What is the reading on the scales?

The reading on the scales is the measure of the force exerted by the scales on the person. We begin by choosing the upward direction as positive. Then *a* is positive if the acceleration is upward and negative if the acceleration is downward. The sign of the acceleration due to gravity is negative since the force of gravity is always downward. Therefore, solving our relationship for F_s, we have

$$F_s = ma - mg = m(a - g) = (90\ kg)[2\ m/s^2 - (-9.81\ m/s^2)] = 1060\ N$$

11 Is It All Relative?

Practice[2]

What is the scale reading if the acceleration is upward at 2 m/s?

◆ ◆ ◆

We can calculate the "g-forces" acting on the person by looking at the ratio of sizes of the force due to the scales to the force due to gravity.

$$g\text{-}force = \frac{F_s}{F_g}$$

As a check we see that for the special case of no acceleration, F_s and F_g have the same sizes. Therefore, the person experiences the normal force of 1 g. An alternate expression can be obtained by substituting our expressions for the two forces.

$$g\text{-}force = \frac{F_s}{F_g} = \frac{ma - mg}{mg} = \frac{a - g}{g}$$

Example 11.2.2

What g-force does the person in Example 9.2.1 experience?

The person experiences a g-force of

$$g\text{-}force = \frac{F_s}{F_g} = \frac{1060\,N}{883\,N} = 1.2\,g$$

Practice[3]

What is the g-force if the elevator is accelerating downward at 2 m/s²?

Example 11.2.3

Assume that our elevator can somehow be accelerated sideways and that the scales can be tilted so that the force of the scales acts in the proper direction to cancel out the force of gravity and provide the necessary sideways acceleration. What is the scale reading if the acceleration of the elevator is 2 m/s²?

The vector form of our relationship is still valid. Therefore, we draw a vector diagram like the one in Fig. 11.2.1. $\mathbf{F_s}$ is equal to the vector difference of $m\mathbf{a}$ and $\mathbf{F_g}$. In this

---

[2] 703 N

[3] 0.8 g

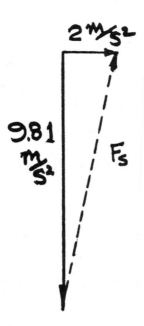

case, the vectors are perpendicular to each other and the size of the vector can be found using the Pythagorean theorem.

$$F_s = \sqrt{F_g^2 + (ma)^2}$$

$$= \sqrt{(883\,N)^2 + (180\,N)^2} = 901\,N$$

Notice that the scale reading does not increase as much as it did in Example 11.2.1. The direction θ of F_s can be measured from the diagram to be 11° from the vertical.

Practice[4]

What is the scale reading if the sideways acceleration is increased to 5 m/s²?

◆ ◆ ◆

Fig. 11.2.1

11.3 Centrifugal Forces

If an object is at rest in a rotating reference system and we wish to explain this through the invention of a fictitious force, we conclude that the centrifugal force is equal in size to the centripetal force but oppositely directed. Therefore, we can use our equations for the size of the centripetal acceleration and centripetal force developed in Section 3.2 to calculate the corresponding sizes for the centrifugal acceleration and force.

$$a_c = \frac{v^2}{r} \qquad\qquad F_c = m\frac{v^2}{r}$$

Example 11.3.1

Assume that a space station with a radius of 1 km is rotating about its center at 1 rev/min. What is the strength of the artificial gravity produced by the centrifugal force?

We begin by calculating the speed of a point on the rim of the space station. This is just the circumference of the station divided by its rotational period, the time it takes to rotate once.

---

[4] 991 N

$$v = \frac{C}{T} = \frac{2\pi r}{T} = \frac{(6.28)(1000\,m)}{60\,s} = 105\,m/s$$

$$a_c = \frac{v^2}{r} = \frac{(105\,m/s)^2}{1000\,m} = 11\,m/s^2$$

Practice[5]

What would the acceleration be if the radius of the space station and the rotational speed are both doubled?

◆ ◆ ◆

11.4 The Earth: A Nearly Inertial System

We do not feel the earth move and it seems that our massive earth is motionless. But, in fact, it is moving at a very high speed. Consider the annual motion of the earth around the sun. Assuming the earth's orbit is circular with a radius of 1.50×10^{11} m and knowing that there are about 3.16×10^7 s in 1 year, we can calculate its speed.

$$v = \frac{C}{T} = \frac{2\pi r}{T} = \frac{(6.28)(1.50 \times 10^{11}\,m)}{3.16 \times 10^7\,s} = 2.98 \times 10^4\,m/s$$

Although this is a fast speed, it may not seem so fast written in this form, so let's convert it to km/h.

$$2.98 \times 10^4\,\frac{m}{s} \left[\frac{1\,km}{1000\,m}\right]\left[\frac{3600\,s}{1\,h}\right] = 107,000\,km/h \qquad (66,500\,mph)$$

In addition, every point on the earth's surface moves in a circular path every 24 hours. A person on the equator travels about 40,000 km (24,900 miles) in 24 hours. This is a speed of 463 m/s = 1670 km/h = 1040 mph.

It is not the speed that determines whether the earth is an inertial system, it is the acceleration. We will calculate the accelerations due to each of these motions in the next section.

---

[5] 88 m/s^2

11.5 Noninertial Effects of the Earth's Motion

The noninertial effects due to the earth's motion are caused by its acceleration, not its velocity. We, therefore, need to calculate the accelerations due to each of its motions to see how much each one contributes.

Let's begin with the acceleration due to the earth's rotation on its axis. We can use the results in the last section to obtain the value.

$$a_c = \frac{v^2}{r} = \frac{(463 \; m/s)^2}{6.37 \times 10^6 \; m} = 3.37 \times 10^{-2} \; m/s^2$$

Since this acceleration is only 0.34% of the acceleration due to gravity at the surface of the earth, it is a relatively small effect.

The same calculation for the earth's revolution around the sun yields

$$a = \frac{v^2}{r} = \frac{(2.98 \times 10^4 \; m/s)^2}{1.50 \times 10^{11} \; m} = 5.92 \times 10^{-3} \; m/s^2$$

which is smaller than the acceleration due to the earth's rotation even though the speed of revolution is a lot larger than the speed for rotation.

Problems

1. A baseball player riding on the bed of a truck traveling at 10 m/s throws a ball with a horizontal speed of 20 m/s. What is the ball's speed relative to the ground if it is thrown (a) forward? (b) backward?

2. A toy cannon is mounted on a flatcar of a model train. If the train travels at 1 m/s and the cannon fires balls with a horizontal speed of 3 m/s, what is the ball's speed relative to the ground if it is fired (a) forward? (b) backward?

3. A spring gun fires a ball horizontally at 40 m/s. It is mounted on a flatcar moving in a straight line at 30 m/s. Relative to the ground, what is the horizontal speed of the ball when the gun is aimed to the side?

4. A train is traveling along a straight, horizontal track at a constant speed of 50 km/h. If a ball is fired forward with a speed of 80 km/h relative to the train, what is its speed relative to the ground? What if it is fired directly to the side?

5. If a child weighs 200 N standing at rest on earth, what is the weight of this child in an elevator being accelerated upward with a constant value of 1 m/s^2?

6. What is the scale reading if a 70-kg dog lies on the scale in an elevator accelerating upward at 2 m/s^2?

7. What is the weight of the child in problem 5 if the acceleration is downward?

8. What is the scale reading for the dog in problem 6 if the acceleration is downward?

9. An observer in a train with an acceleration of 10 m/s^2 notices that a ball falls in a straight line that is slanted toward the back of the train. What is the acceleration of the ball along this line?

10. What is the angle of the ball's path in the previous problem?

*11. A ball is dropped from a height of 1 m in a train traveling at 20 m/s and accelerating at 1 m/s^2. By how far will the ball miss the spot directly below where it was dropped?

*12. A ball is dropped from a height of 2 m in a train traveling at 30 m/s and accelerating at 2 m/s^2. By how far will the ball miss the spot directly below where it was dropped?

13. What is the acceleration due to artificial gravity if a space station has a radius of 1000 m and rotates at 2 rpm? How does this compare to the value of *g* on earth?

14. What is the acceleration at the rim of a merry-go-round if it has a radius of 2 m and makes one revolution every 4 s? How does this value compare to the acceleration due to gravity?

15. What is the centrifugal acceleration on the equator of Mars if it has a rotational period of 24.6 h?

16. What is the centrifugal acceleration on the equator of the moon if it has a rotational period of 27.3 days?

17. What is the average speed of Venus in its orbit about the sun?

18. With what average speed does Mars orbit the sun?

19. Calculate the acceleration of the earth due to its motion around the center of the Milky Way Galaxy. Assume that the orbital radius is about 3 x 10^{17} km and the orbital period is 2.5 x 10^8 years. How does this acceleration compare to the value of g?

20. What is the acceleration of Mars around the sun?

*21. A ball dropped at latitudes corresponding to those of the USA does not fall vertically, but lands to the east of the point directly under the point of release. This is often explained by the Coriolis force. Show that this is simply a consequence of the conservation of angular momentum (Chapter 5) if the motion is viewed from an inertial reference system.

12 THE SPECIAL THEORY OF RELATIVITY

12.1 Searching for the Medium of Light

The predicted results for the Michelson-Morley experiment can be illustrated using a more common example of two boats racing along perpendicular paths on a river. Here, the analog of the ether wind is the river's current. The boats start at the same point and travel equal distances at equal speeds <u>relative to the water</u> but in different directions. We will use the symbol c (normally reserved for the speed of light) for the boats' speeds and v for the speed of the current to further highlight the analogy.

Suppose the first boat's path is parallel to the current, and the second boat's path is perpendicular to the current. The first boat travels downstream a distance L, turns around instantaneously, and returns to the starting point, as shown in Fig. 12.1.1. The second boat travels straight across the river, again a distance L, and returns.

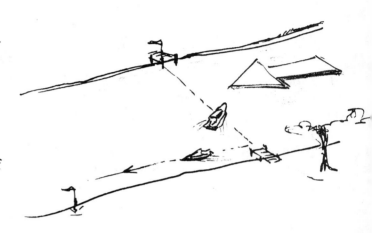

Fig. 12.1.1

For the first boat the time t_{1d} to travel downstream is obtained by dividing the distance traveled by the speed of the boat relative to the shore (See Section 11.1). This speed is the sum of the speed of the boat relative to the water plus that of the water relative to the shore. If we assume a boat speed of 3 m/s, a current of 1 m/s, and a distance of 1200 m, we obtain

$$t_{1d} = \frac{L}{c+v} = \frac{1200\ m}{3\ m/s + 1\ m/s} = 300\ s$$

The time t_{1u} that it takes the boat to return upstream is given by

$$t_{1u} = \frac{L}{c-v} = \frac{1200\ m}{3\ m/s - 1\ m/s} = 600\ s$$

This gives a total time t_1 for the round trip of 900 s.

In order for the second boat to travel straight across the river, it must aim upstream. This reduces its speed across the river. We can find this speed by requiring that the velocity of the boat plus the velocity of the current add to point straight across the river as shown in Fig. 12.1.2. The speed of 2.83 m/s can be obtained graphically as we did in Chapter 3 in the text or by using the Pythagorean theorem (Section 3.1). Using this value, we calculate the time t_2 to travel across the river to be

$$t_2 = \frac{1200\ m}{2.83\ m/s} = 424\ s$$

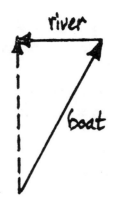

Fig. 12.1.2

Since the trip back takes the same amount of time, the total round-trip time is 848 s. Therefore, the second boat arrives back at the finish line 52 s before the first boat even though the boats are identical. The puzzle for physicists at the turn of the century was that the light beams came back at the same time!

12.2 Experimental Evidence for Time Dilation

The size of the time-dilation effect can be calculated precisely using the Pythagorean theorem. First, let's consider the time as seen by an observer at rest relative to the clock. In this system the light beam travels straight up to the mirror and returns as shown in Fig. 12.2.1(a). It travels a distance equal to twice the length of the light clock. This requires a time t_o

$$t_o = \frac{2L}{c}$$

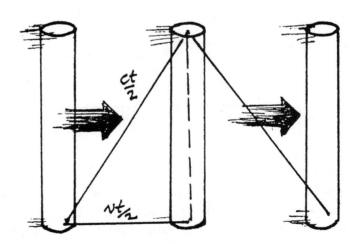

Fig. 12.2.1

The distance traveled by the light beam in the moving reference system depends on the relative speed of the moving system. Figure 12.2.1(b) shows the distances the light beam travels (as seen by an observer in the rest system) in terms of the speed multiplied by the total time t. The Pythagorean theorem for the left-hand triangle is

$$\left[\frac{ct}{2}\right]^2 - \left[\frac{vt}{2}\right]^2 = L^2$$

To obtain a relationship between the times in the two systems, we substitute for L from the at-rest system to obtain

$$\left[\frac{ct}{2}\right]^2 - \left[\frac{vt}{2}\right]^2 = \left[\frac{ct_o}{2}\right]^2$$

Solving for the time t in the moving system yields the amount that the time is dilated as viewed from the rest system.

$$t = \frac{1}{\sqrt{1 - (v/c)^2}} \, t_o = \gamma \, t_o$$

where γ is the adjustment factor for special relativity. Some values of γ are listed in Table 12-1 in the text.

Example 12.2.1

How much is the time dilation for $v = c/2$?

Let's begin by calculating the adjustment factor γ.

$$\gamma = \frac{1}{\sqrt{1 - (v/c)^2}} = \frac{1}{\sqrt{1 - (\frac{1}{2})^2}} = \frac{1}{\sqrt{\frac{3}{4}}} = \sqrt{\frac{4}{3}} = 1.15$$

Therefore $t = 1.15t_o$. This means that an event that takes 1 s in the at-rest system is viewed as taking 1.15 s when it is viewed from the moving system. It is important to realize that this works both ways. One second for observers in the moving system lasts 1.15 s when viewed by observers in the at-rest system.

Practice[1]

What is the adjustment factor for a speed of $0.75c$?

---

[1] 1.51

Example 12.2.2

What speed is required for time to be slowed by a factor of 2?

We start with our expression for the adjustment factor, solve it for v, and set $\gamma = 2$.

$$v = c\sqrt{1 - \frac{1}{\gamma^2}} = c\sqrt{1 - \frac{1}{4}} = c\sqrt{\frac{3}{4}} = 0.866\,c$$

Practice[2]

What speed is required for a time dilation by a factor of 4?

◆ ◆ ◆

12.3 Comparing Velocities

We have already seen that the second postulate requires a new rule for connecting velocities measured in two different inertial reference systems. Although the derivation of the new rule is beyond the mathematical level of this manual, we give the rule to illustrate how two velocities close to the speed of light can be added without exceeding the speed of light.

Assume that the relative speed of system #2 as measured in system #1 is v. Assume further that our object has speed u_2 as measured in system #2 and that the object is moving parallel to the relative velocity. Then the speed u_1 measured in the first system is

$$u_1 = \frac{u_2 + v}{1 + \frac{u_2 v}{c^2}}$$

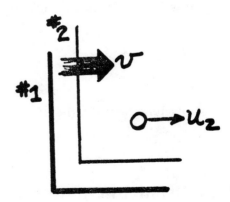

This rule has the same form as the classical rule except for the term in the denominator. Notice that the rule reduces to the classical rule if u_2 is very much less than c since the value of the denominator is very close to 1. This must be the case since the classical rule worked very well for small velocities.

Fig. 12.3.1

Example 12.3.1

It is interesting to look at the extreme situation where the speed in the moving system is c and the system is moving with a speed very, very close to c. What is u_1?

---

[2] 0.968 c

In this case, we set $u_2 = c$ and $v = c$ in the rule. This yields a value for u_1 of c as required by the second postulate.

$$u_1 = \frac{u_2 + v}{1 + \frac{u_2 v}{c^2}} = \frac{c + c}{1 + \frac{cc}{c^2}} = \frac{2c}{2} = c$$

Practice[3]

If the object has a speed of c/2 in system #2 and the relative speed is c/2, what is the speed of the object in system #1?

◆ ◆ ◆

12.4 Length Contraction

The length of a moving object L measured along its direction of motion is equal to its length L_0 measured by an observer at rest relative to the object divided by the relativistic adjustment factor. Therefore,

$$L = \frac{L_o}{\gamma}$$

Example 12.4.1

How long is a meter stick moving at $0.8c$ along its length?

$$L = \frac{L_o}{\gamma} = L_o\sqrt{1 - (v/c)^2} = (1\,m)\sqrt{1 - 0.8^2} = 0.6\,m$$

Practice[4]

How long will the meter stick be if its speed is $0.9c$?

◆ ◆ ◆

12.5 Relativistic Laws of Motion

The classical form of Newton's second law carries over into special relativity if we write it in terms of momentum and use the relativistic form for the momentum.

---

[3] 4c/5

[4] 0.436 m

$$F = \frac{\Delta p}{t} = \frac{\Delta(\gamma m v)}{t}$$

Example 12.5.1

A proton in a moderately strong electric field experiences an electric force of 10^{-14} N. How long would it take this field to accelerate the proton from rest to 80% of the speed of light?

At this speed the relativistic adjustment factor is equal to 1.67. We solve the relativistic form of Newton's second law for the time t, set the initial momentum equal to zero, and plug in the known values.

$$t = \frac{\gamma m v}{F} = \frac{(1.67)(1.67 \times 10^{-27} \, kg)(0.8 \times 3 \times 10^8 \, m/s)}{10^{-14} \, N} = 66.9 \, \mu s$$

If we increase the final speed to 90% of c, the time increases to 103 μs. Therefore, it requires 36 μs to increase the speed from 80% to 90% c. It takes half as long to gain the last 10% as it did to gain the original 80%. If we continue this trend, it will require an additional 50 μs to increase the speed from 90% to 95% c, half the gain in a longer time. Each additional gain requires longer and longer to accomplish, increasing very rapidly as we approach c, the limiting speed.

Practice[5]

How long would it take this force to accelerate the proton from rest to $0.99c$?

◆ ◆ ◆

12.6 Relativistic Energy

Example 12.6.1

What is the rest-mass energy of a proton?

$$E_o = mc^2 = (1.67 \times 10^{-27} \, kg)(3 \times 10^8 \, m/s)^2 = 1.5 \times 10^{-10} \, J$$

Example 12.6.2

What is the total energy of a proton traveling at $0.9c$?

---

[5] 352 μs

$$E = \gamma m c^2 = (2.29)(1.67 \times 10^{-27} kg)(3 \times 10^8 m/s)^2 = 3.44 \times 10^{-10} J$$

Note that this answer is larger than that in Example 12.6.1 by the relativistic adjustment factor. If you use the concept of a relativistic mass, the proton traveling at 0.9c has a mass that is 2.29 times larger that when it is a rest.

Practice[6]

What is the total energy of a proton traveling at 0.95c?

◆ ◆ ◆

Problems

1. When Mars appears in the southern sky around midnight, it is approximately 75 million km from earth. How long would it take to bounce a radar signal from Mars' surface and detect the returning signal?

2. The Andromeda galaxy is approximately 2×10^{19} km from our sun. How long would it take light from this galaxy to reach us?

3. A boat race takes place on a river with a current of 5 km/h. If the boats have speeds of 30 km/h relative to the water, how long would it take to complete a race that goes 60 km up the river and back? How much longer does it take than for the same race on a lake?

*4. Knowing that the orbital speed of the earth is 100,000 km/h, what is the maximum time difference Michelson and Morley could have expected if each arm of their apparatus were 1 m long?

5. How much is time dilated for a speed of 0.9c?

6. How much would a clock lose in 1 year if it were traveling at 0.1c?

7. What is the adjustment factor for a speed of 0.5c?

8. What is the adjustment factor for a speed of 0.99c?

9. The idea behind the Movie <u>Buck Rogers in the 25th Century</u> is theoretically possible. With what speed would Buck have to travel in order to age only 5 years in 500 years of traveling?

10. If you wanted to travel a distance of 10 light years while aging only 1 year, how fast would you need to travel?

11. If a particle has a speed of 0.5c toward the front of a space ship that is traveling away from earth at 0.9c, what is the speed of the particle relative to earth?

12. What is the speed of the particle in the previous problem if the particle is traveling toward the back of the space ship?

---

[6] 4.81×10^{-10} J

13. A particle traveling at $0.9c$ in the laboratory decays by emitting a particle with a speed of $0.9c$ measured in the particle's reference system. If the decay is in the forward direction, what is the speed of the decay particle in the laboratory?

14. What is the speed of the decay particle in the previous problem if both speeds are $0.99c$?

15. What is the length of a meter stick traveling at $0.5c$ in a direction along its length?

16. The distance to the nearest star (other than our own sun) is 4.2×10^{16} m. How far away is this star when observed from a space ship traveling at $0.99c$?

*17. How fast would a meter stick have to be moving to be 60 cm long?

*18. If you want to fit a 10-m pole into a 3-m shed, how fast must it be moving?

19. What impulse is needed to accelerate a proton from rest to $0.9c$?

20. What impulse is needed to accelerate an electron from rest to $0.9c$?

21. What average force is needed to accelerate a proton from rest to $0.9c$ in 1 μs?

22. What average force is needed to accelerate an electron from rest to $0.9c$ in 1 μs?

23. What is the rest-mass energy of an electron?

24. What is the rest-mass energy of a neutron?

25. If the total energy of a muon is 3 times its rest-mass energy, how fast must it be moving?

26. How fast must a proton be moving for its rest-mass energy to be only 10% of its total energy?

*27. By what factor does the relativistic momentum increase when the speed doubles from 0.3c to 0.6c?

13   GENERAL RELATIVITY

13.1 Gravity and Acceleration

The equivalence principle states that *a constant acceleration is completely equivalent to a uniform gravitational field*. This means that doing physics in a space ship with a constant acceleration in deep space is just like doing physics on the surface of a planet with an acceleration due to gravity equal to the acceleration of the space ship. Therefore, being in a space ship with an acceleration of 9.81 m/s² is just like being on earth. The direction of this relativistic gravitational field is always opposite the direction of the acceleration. If the acceleration takes place in the presence of a gravitational field, we can find the effective gravity g_{eff} by combining the actual gravitational field g with that due to the acceleration g_{rel}.

Example 13.1.1

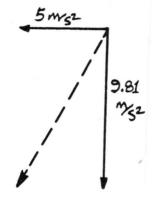

A train is traveling down a long, straight track with a constant acceleration of 5 m/s² is the forward direction. If a passenger in the train drops a ball, what is the path of the ball and how large is its acceleration as viewed in the train.

The acceleration of the train is equivalent to a gravitational field g_{rel} in the backward direction that produces an acceleration of the ball equal to 5 m/s². We must add this to the normal gravitational field on earth that produces an acceleration of 9.81 m/s² downward.

Fig. 13.1.1

Remembering that both of these are vectors, we can add them using our graphical method as shown in Fig. 13.1.1. The path is obtained by measuring the angle on the graph. The ball falls along a straight line tilted backward 27° from the vertical.

We can also obtain the magnitude of the effective acceleration using the Pythagorean theorem.

$$g_{eff} = \sqrt{g_{rel}^2 + g^2} = \sqrt{(5\ m/s^2)^2 + (9.81\ m/s^2)^2} = 11\ m/s^2$$

Practice[1]

At what angle and with what acceleration would the ball fall if the train's acceleration were 10 m/s²?

---

[1] 14.2 m/s² at 45° from the vertical.

13.2 Gravity and Light

Example 13.2.1

How much would a horizontal beam of light fall in 9 m?

As this is a problem in projectile motion, we begin by calculating the time for the light to travel 9 m horizontally.

$$t = \frac{d}{v} = \frac{9\,m}{3 \times 10^8\,m/s} = 3 \times 10^{-8}\,s$$

We can now plug this time into our equation for the distance fallen from rest in free fall.

$$d = \frac{1}{2}gt^2 = \frac{1}{2}(9.81\,m/s^2)(3 \times 10^{-8}\,s)^2 = 4.41 \times 10^{-15}\,m$$

Because the diameter of an atom is typically 10^{-10} m, we see that the light beam falls much less than the diameter of an atom as stated in the text.

◆ ◆ ◆

Problems

1. A fast-growing bean stock grows in a train with a constant acceleration of 1 m/s². What angle does the stock make with the floor of the train?

2. What is the effective gravity in a train with a constant acceleration of 20 m/s²?

3. By how much would a horizontal beam of light fall while traveling across a 20-m wide room?

4. If the speed of light were only 2000 m/s, by how much would a horizontal beam of light fall in traveling across a 20-m wide room?

5. What is the acceleration due to gravity at the surface of the sun? How does this compare to the value for *g* on earth?

6. What is the acceleration due to gravity at the surface of a neutron star that has a mass of 4 x 10³⁰ kg (twice that of the sun) and a radius of 10 km?

14 VIBRATIONS AND WAVES

14.1 Simple Vibrations

For our relationship between period and frequency to work properly, we must be sure that the frequency is stated in cycles per unit time, or an equivalent expression such as revolutions per unit time. [Note that cycles and revolutions are not units in the usual sense that they must be carried through equations.] Sometimes we are given the rotational speed instead of the frequency. In such cases, we must convert these rotational speeds to frequencies in order to calculate the periods.

Example 14.1.1

What are the frequency and period of a disk rotating with a rotational speed of 18°/s?

$$f = \frac{18°}{1\ s}\left[\frac{1\ rev}{360°}\right] = 0.05\ rev/s$$

$$T = \frac{1}{f} = \frac{1}{0.05\ rev/s} = 20\ s$$

Practice[1]

What happens to the period if the frequency is doubled?

♦ ♦ ♦

14.2 Period of a Mass on a Spring

When two springs with identical spring constants k are placed side-by-side, we can define an effective spring constant k_{eff} for the combination. Because we have to pull with twice the force to get the same displacement, the spring constant for the combination must be twice as large. In general, $k_{eff} = k_1 + k_2$.

Example 14.2.1

The spring constant for a car's suspension system is a result of the parallel arrangement of four springs. If one of the springs was tested in the lab and determined to have a spring constant of 10^4 N/m, and the car's mass is 1600 kg, with what period will the car oscillate?

Generalizing the case for two springs in parallel, we expect that the effective spring

---

[1] It is half as big.

constant will be 4 times the value of one of them, or 4 x 10^4 N/m. Therefore, the period is given by

$$T = 2\pi \sqrt{\frac{m}{k_{eff}}} = 2\pi \sqrt{\frac{1600\,kg}{4 \times 10^4\,N/m}} = \frac{4\pi}{10}\,s = 1.26\,s$$

Practice[2]

A mass on the end of a spring oscillates with a period of 1 s. What will the period be if the mass is attached to two of these springs placed side-by-side?

We can also consider the case of two springs with identical spring constants placed end-to-end. Because the applied force is felt by both springs, we get twice the displacement for the same force. Therefore, the effective value of the spring constant is one-half of either spring constant.

Example 14.2.2

What happens to the spring constant when you cut a spring in half?

Because this is the opposite of connecting two springs end-to-end, we would expect the spring constant to be twice as large.

14.3 Period of a Pendulum

The formula for the period of a pendulum developed in the text assumes that the string is massless and that the mass is concentrated at a point. In practice, two pendula with the same length string can have different periods if the bobs have different sizes. Careful study shows that the length of the pendulum is actually the distance from the support point to the center of mass of the bob if the length of the string is large compared to the size of the bob.

If the string has mass, or if the whole object is swinging back and forth, we have to modify our relationship to take this into account. As an example of a more complicated pendulum, consider a meterstick swinging from one end. The period for such a *physical* pendulum is given by

$$T = 2\pi \sqrt{\frac{I}{mgh}}$$

where I is the rotational inertia of the object about the pivot point, h is the distance from the

---

[2] 0.707 s

pivot point to the center of mass of the object, m is the object's mass, and g is the acceleration due to gravity.

Example 14.3.1

What is the period of a meterstick swinging from one end?

We saw in Section 3.5 that the rotational inertia of a rod is

$$I = \frac{1}{3} mL^2$$

The value of h is $L/2$ because the center of mass is at the middle of the meterstick. Therefore, the period of the swinging meterstick is

$$T = 2\pi \sqrt{\frac{2L}{3g}} = 2\pi \sqrt{\frac{2m}{3(9.81 \; m/s^2)}} = 1.64 \; s$$

◆ ◆ ◆

Let's check to make sure that this new relationship reduces to the previous result for a simple pendulum. The rotational inertia of a point mass m moving along a circular path of radius r is mr^2 (Section 3-5). Substituting this into the relationship yields

$$T = 2\pi \sqrt{\frac{I}{mgh}} = 2\pi \sqrt{\frac{mr^2}{mgr}} = 2\pi \sqrt{\frac{r}{g}}$$

where r is the distance from the pivot point to the center of mass of the bob.

As fascinating as what affects the period of the pendulum is what does *not* affect it. Notice that the mass and the amplitude are not in the relationship for the period. The absence of the amplitude means that the period remains constant (at least to a good approximation) as the motion dies down.

Example 14.3.2

The period of a pendulum can be used as an experimental method for determining the value of g. Suppose a student on a distant planet measures the period of a 1-m pendulum to be 3.14 s. What is the value of the acceleration due to gravity on this planet?

Rearranging the relationship we get

$$g = \frac{4\pi^2}{T^2} L = \frac{4\pi^2}{(3.14 \; s)^2} (1 \; m) = 4 \; m/s^2$$

Practice[3]

What would you expect for the period of a 1.7-m pendulum on the moon where the acceleration is one-sixth that on earth?

Example 14.3.3

Suppose you want to make a clock with a pendulum that has a period of 1 s. How long should the pendulum be?

We begin by solving our relationship for the length and then plugging in the given values.

$$L = \left[\frac{T}{2\pi}\right]^2 g = \left[\frac{1\,s}{6.28}\right]^2 (9.81\,m/s^2) = 0.249\,m$$

Practice[4]

How long must a pendulum be to have a period of 2 s?

◆ ◆ ◆

14.4 One-Dimensional Waves

The speed of a wave can be determined in the same manner as you would determine the speed of a car. You simply measure how far the wave travels in a given amount of time.

Example 14.4.1

If it takes the thunder 11.7 s to reach you from a lightning bolt that strikes a tree 4 km away, what is the speed of sound?

$$v = \frac{d}{t} = \frac{4000\,m}{11.7\,s} = 342\,m/s$$

Practice[5]

What is the speed of a wave that travels down a 20-m rope in 3 s?

---

[3] 6.4 s

[4] 0.995 m

[5] 6.67 m/s

14.5 Superposition

Example 14.5.1

The two idealized wave pulses shown in Fig. 14.5.1 are traveling in opposite directions along a rope with speeds of 1 m/s. What is the resultant shape of the rope 2 s, 3 s, and 4 s later.

We obtain the shape by redrawing each shape at the new time as if the other shape were not present and adding the displacements of the two waves together. The displacement of each wave is the amount the rope has moved from its equilibrium position with one direction positive and the other negative.

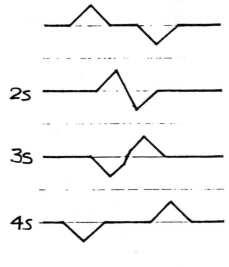

Fig. 14.5.1

14.6 Periodic Waves

The speed v, wavelength λ, and frequency f of periodic waves are always related by the basic equation derived in the text.

$$v = \lambda f$$

This equation can be rearranged to get the wavelength in terms of the speed and the frequency or it can be solved for the frequency to obtain its value in terms of the speed and the wavelength.

Example 14.6.1

A periodic wave has a speed of 1500 m/s and a frequency of 50 Hz. What is its wavelength?

$$\lambda = \frac{v}{f} = \frac{1500 \, m/s}{50 \, Hz} = \frac{1500 \, m/s}{50 /s} = 30 \, m$$

Practice[6]

What would the wavelength be if the frequency were increased to 3000 Hz?

Example 14.6.2

What is the frequency of a periodic wave with a wavelength of 40 m and a velocity of 5000 m/s?

$$f = \frac{v}{\lambda} = \frac{5000 \; m/s}{40 \; m} = 125 \; Hz$$

◆ ◆ ◆

14.7 Standing Waves

Fig. 14.7.1

The key to determining the possible standing wave patterns is knowing what happens at each end of the medium. For instance, if a rope is fixed at both ends, there will be nodes at each end as shown in Figs. 14-20, 14-21, and 14-22 in the text. However, if the rope is hung vertically, the lower end will be free. Then there will be a node at the upper end and an antinode at the lower end. Since the distance between adjacent nodes and antinodes is one-fourth wavelength, the longest wavelength that will fit on the rope is four times the length of the rope L as shown in Fig. 14.7.1. Thus, the fundamental wavelength $\lambda_o = 4L$.

If we now shorten the wavelength, we find that the next pattern that will fit on the rope is one-third λ_o as shown in Fig. 14.7.2. The next shorter wavelength is one-fifth λ_o, and so on.
The pattern for the wavelengths can be written as

Fig. 14.7.2

$$\lambda = \frac{4L}{1}, \; \frac{4L}{3}, \; \frac{4L}{5}, \; \frac{4L}{7}, \; \dots$$

14.8 Frequencies of Standing Waves

Once we know the wavelength of a standing wave, we can calculate its frequency if we know the speed of the waves in the medium. The relationship between speed, wavelength, and frequency for periodic waves holds since a standing wave is just a superposition of two periodic waves traveling in opposite directions.

---

[6] 0.5 m

Example 14.8.1

What is the frequency of the fundamental standing wave on a 5-m rope fixed at both ends if the waves travel at 2 m/s?

As indicated in the text, the fundamental standing wave will have the longest wavelength. When both ends are fixed, the longest wavelength is twice the length of the rope. Therefore, $\lambda = 10$ m.

$$f = \frac{v}{\lambda} = \frac{2\,m/s}{10\,m} = 0.2\,Hz$$

Practice[7]

What is the frequency of the second harmonic?

◆ ◆ ◆

14.9 Interference

Assume that we have two point sources of water waves that are the same distances away from a distant wall as shown in Fig. 14.9.1. If the two sources are in phase, the central antinodal line will be perpendicular to the wall. The relative locations where the other antinodal lines intersect the wall can be obtained with the following formula.

$$y_{max} = m\,\frac{\lambda L}{d} \qquad m = \pm1, \pm2, \pm3, ...$$

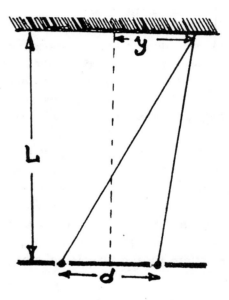

Fig. 14.9.1

where y_{max} is the distance measured along the wall from the central bright region, λ is the wavelength, L is the distance to the wall, d is the spacing of the slits, and m is an integer that numbers the antinodal lines beginning with m = 0 at the center.

Example 14.9.1

Two sources of water waves with a spacing of 5 cm are 1 m from a wall. If the

---

[7] 0.4 Hz

wavelength of the water waves is 2 cm, what is the spacing of the antinodal lines along the wall?

Since we know that the central antinodal line is at $y = 0$, we can get the spacing by setting $m = 1$.

$$y = m\frac{\lambda L}{d} = (1)\frac{(2\,cm)(1\,m)}{5\,cm} = 0.4\,m$$

Therefore, the spacing between antinodal regions is 0.4 m. If we were to choose $m = 5$ and $m = 6$, we would get the same answer.

Practice[8]

What is the spacing if the wavelength is reduced to 1 cm?

◆ ◆ ◆

14.10 Diffraction

An expression similar to the one in the last section gives the locations of the nodal positions from a diffraction pattern produced by a slit of width w.

$$y_{min} = m\frac{\lambda L}{w} \qquad\qquad m = \pm 1, \pm 2, \pm 3, \ldots$$

Notice that $m = 0$ is excluded. This occurs because the central region is an antinodal region. This central region is twice as wide as the other antinodal regions.

Example 14.10.1

Waves pass through a 4-cm slit and strike a wall 1 m away. If the wavelength is 2 cm, how wide is the central maximum?

We can calculate the width of the central maximum by determining the locations of the minima on either side. Using our formula with $m = \pm 1$, we have

$$y_{min} = m\frac{\lambda L}{w} = (\pm 1)\frac{(2\,cm)(1\,m)}{4\,cm} = \pm 0.5\,m$$

Therefore, the central maximum is 1 m wide.

---

[8] 0.2 m

Practice[9]

What is the width of the central maximum if the slit width is increased to 8 cm?

◆ ◆ ◆

Problems

1. A bob oscillates on a vertical spring. If the frequency of the motion is 5 Hz, what is its period?
2. What is the period of a mass on a spring that oscillates with a frequency of 3 Hz?
3. A platter rotates with a rotational speed of 20°/s. What are the frequency and period of the platter's motion?
4. If a wheel rotates at 100 radians/s, what are its frequency and period? There are 2π radians in a complete circle.
5. A 1-kg mass is suspended from a spring with a spring constant of 1600 N/m. What is the system's period of oscillation?
6. A 1500-kg car is suspended by four springs that behave like one spring with a spring constant of 12,000 N/m. What is the period for oscillations of the car?
7. If a 0.5-kg block suspended from the end of a spring oscillates with a frequency of 0.2 Hz, what is the value of the spring constant?
8. What spring constant is required for a 0.1-kg mass to have a frequency of oscillation equal to 4 Hz?
9. A spring has a spring constant of 200 N/m. What mass is needed to obtain an oscillation with a period of 0.5 s?

10. What mass is needed for a resonant frequency of 4 s if the spring has a spring constant of 1000 N/m?
11. If a grandfather clock has a pendulum with a length of 1.2 m, what is its period?
12. A Foucault pendulum has a length of 12 m. What is its period?
13. What length is required to build a pendulum with a period of 4 s?
14. What length is required to build a pendulum with a period of 10 s?
15. If a 1-m long pendulum on the moon has a period of 4.9 s, what is the acceleration due to gravity near the surface of the moon?
16. If a 1-m long pendulum on Mars has a period of 3.26 s, what is the acceleration due to gravity on Mars?
17. A pendulum with a length of 2 m has a period of 2.8 s. What is the period of a pendulum with a length of 8 m?
18. A mass of 2 kg hanging from a certain spring oscillates with a frequency of 10 Hz. What would the frequency be if the mass were changed to 8 kg?
19. A wave pulse travels the length of a 12-m clothesline in 3 s. What is the speed of the pulse?
20. An earthquake on the floor of the ocean near Alaska creates a tidal wave that

---

[9] 0.5 m

hits the Hawaiian Islands 7 h later. If the tidal wave traveled 4400 km, what was the average speed of the wave?

21. In Fig. 14.P.1, two idealized wave pulses are traveling on a rope in opposite directions with speeds of 1 m/s. What are the shapes of the rope after 2 s, 3 s, 4 s, and 6 s?

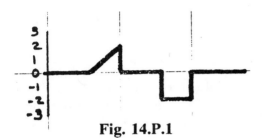

Fig. 14.P.1

22. Work Problem 21 with the right-hand pulse inverted top for bottom.

23. If sound waves travel at 340 m/s, what is the wavelength of a musical note with a frequency of 256 Hz?

24. If 2-Hz waves on a rope travel at 2 m/s, what is their wavelength?

*25. While standing on a dock, you observe water waves passing beneath you. Being highly motivated in physics, you count 30 wave crests passing directly below you in one minute and judge the crests to be 0.5 m apart. What are the frequency, period, and speed of the waves?

*26. If the fundamental frequency for a 2-m long rope fixed at both ends is 5 Hz, what is the speed of the wave?

27. What possible wavelengths will produce longitudinal standing waves in a 1-m long rod that is clamped at one end?

*28. What possible wavelengths will produce longitudinal standing waves in a 1-m long rod that is clamped at its center?

29. What is the frequency of the fundamental standing wave produced on a 5-m long rope if the speed of the waves is 10 m/s?

30. If the speed of sound is 343 m/s, what is the lowest frequency sound that will form a standing wave in a 1-m long tube with nodes at both ends?

31. Two audio speakers separated by 3 m produce sound waves with a wavelength of 0.5 m. At what points along a facing wall do you expect to hear loud sounds if the wall is 3 m away, if the speed of sound is 343 m/s, and the speakers are in phase?

32. The two probes in a rectangular ripple tank produce waves with a wavelength of 0.5 cm. If the separation of the probes is 2 cm and the far side of the tank is 50 cm away, where would you expect the largest waves to hit the side?

33. Sound waves with a frequency of 1000 Hz and a speed of 343 m/s are incident on a doorway with a width of 80 cm. What is the width of the central maximum on a wall opposite the doorway if the wall is 4 m away?

34. Ocean waves with a wavelength of 10 m and a frequency of 0.2 s strike an opening in a seawall straight on. If a flat beach is parallel to the seawall and 40 m from it, where on the beach will the water flow the farthest inland?

15   SOUND AND MUSIC

15.1 Speed of Sound

The speed of sound in a gas depends on the temperature of the gas and the type of gas. Because we will usually be dealing with the speed of sound in air, a mixture of gases, we will only take a look at the temperature dependence. Experimental measurements and theoretical arguments both agree that the speed of sound in air at various temperatures can be calculated from

$$v = v_o \sqrt{\frac{T}{T_o}}$$

where v_o is the speed at some reference temperature T_o and v is the speed at some other temperature T. It is necessary to use Kelvin temperatures in this formula. Let's use the values given in the text as our reference values, that is, $v_o = 343$ m/s when $T_o = 20°C = 293$ K.

Example 15.1.1

What is the speed of sound high in the atmosphere where the temperature is -40°C?

Converting the new temperature to Kelvin, we have $T = 273$ K - 40°C = 233 K.

$$v = v_o \sqrt{\frac{T}{T_o}} = (343\,m/s) \sqrt{\frac{233}{293}} = 306\,m/s$$

Practice[1]

What is the speed of sound in air at a temperature of 0°C?

◆ ◆ ◆

15.2 Hearing Sounds

As stated in the text, every increase in the intensity of a sound wave by a factor of 10 means an increase in the sound level by 10 dB. To have a definite scale, some reference intensity must be chosen. By convention 0 db has been chosen to correspond to the threshold of

---

[1] 331 m/s

hearing, which has an intensity of 10^{-12} W/m². We can then calculate any other sound level β from the relationship

$$\beta = (10\,dB)\log\left[\frac{I}{I_o}\right]$$

where log means that you keep only the power of ten in the ratio of I/I_o. If the ratio does not yield a whole number for the factors of ten, you can still obtain an answer by putting the ratio into a calculator and pushing the "log" button.

Example 15.2.1

Let's verify the entry for pain (120 db) shown in the table on page 326 of the text.

Because the sound intensity of a rock concert is about 1 W/m²,

$$\beta = (10\,dB)\log\left[\frac{I}{I_o}\right] = (10\,dB)\log\left[\frac{1\,W/m^2}{10^{-12}\,W/m^2}\right]$$

$$= (10\,dB)\log(10^{12}) = (10\,dB)12 = 120\,dB$$

Practice[2]

What is the sound level for an intensity of 10^3 W/m²?

◆ ◆ ◆

15.3 Stringed Instruments

As shown in the text, the possible wavelengths that can form standing waves on a string fixed at both ends are given by

$$\lambda_n = \frac{2L}{n}$$

where λ_n is the wavelength of the nth harmonic and L is the length of the string. We see that the length of the fundamental wavelength is just $2L$.

Because we know the relationship between speed, wavelength, and frequency, we can write down the possible frequencies.

---

[2] 150 dB

$$f_n = \frac{v}{\lambda_n} = n\left(\frac{v}{2L}\right)$$

We see that the possible frequencies are just whole-number multiples of the fundamental frequency, $v/2L$.

Example 15.3.1

The tension in a guitar string with a length of 80 cm is increased until waves travel along it with a speed of 419 m/s. What are the wavelengths and frequencies of the first three harmonics?

$$\lambda_n = \frac{2L}{n} = \frac{160\,cm}{n} = 160\,cm,\ 80\,cm,\ 53.3\,cm \qquad for\ n = 1,\ 2,\ 3$$

$$f_n = n\left(\frac{v}{2L}\right) = n\left(\frac{419\,m/s}{1.6\,m}\right) = n\,(262\,Hz)$$

$$= 262\,Hz,\ 524\,Hz,\ 786\,Hz \qquad for\ n = 1,\ 2,\ 3$$

Practice[3]

What are the wavelength and frequency of the fourth harmonic?

◆ ◆ ◆

15.4 Wind Instruments

If the wind instrument is open at both ends, there is an antinode at each end. This gives the same possible wavelengths and frequencies described in the previous section. On the other hand, if one end is open and the other closed, the possible wavelengths and frequencies change. As described in the text, the fundamental wavelength is four times the length of the tube and only the odd-numbered harmonics are possible. Therefore, the possible wavelengths and frequencies are given by

$$\lambda_n = \frac{4L}{n} \qquad\qquad \text{where n is odd}$$

---

[3] $\lambda = 40$ cm; f = 1048 Hz

$$f_n = \frac{v}{\lambda_n} = n\left(\frac{v}{4L}\right) \qquad \text{where n is odd}$$

Example 15.4.1

What are the wavelengths and frequencies of the first three harmonics for a closed organ pipe with a length of 60 cm?

Assuming that we can use the room temperature value for the speed of sound, we have

$$\lambda_n = \frac{4L}{n} = \frac{4\,(0.6\,m)}{n} = \frac{2.4\,m}{n}$$

$$= 2.4\,m,\ 0.8\,m,\ 0.48\,m \qquad \text{for } n = 1,\ 3,\ 5$$

$$f_n = n\left(\frac{v}{4L}\right) = n\left(\frac{343\,m/s}{2.4\,m}\right) = n\,(143\,Hz)$$

$$= 143\,Hz,\ 429\,Hz,\ 715\,Hz \qquad \text{for } n = 1,\ 3,\ 5$$

Practice[4]

What are the wavelength and frequency for the next higher harmonic?

◆ ◆ ◆

15.5 Beats

When two sound waves of different frequencies are traveling together in the same direction, the superposition of the two waves produces beats like those shown in Fig. 15-11(c) in the text. We hear a sound with a frequency equal to the average of the two frequencies which varies in amplitude with a frequency that is equal to the difference in the two frequencies. As mentioned in the text, this phenomenon can be used to tune two strings to the same frequency.

Example 15.5.1

When a key on a piano is pressed. the tuner hears a beat frequency of 3 Hz. If one of the strings is know to have a frequency of 262 Hz. what is the frequency of the other?

---

[4] $\lambda = 0.343$ m; f = 1000 Hz

The two strings must differ in frequency by 3 Hz to produce this beat frequency, but we do not know which string has the higher frequency. Therefore, the other string could have a frequency of 259 Hz or 265 Hz.

◆ ◆ ◆

15.6 Doppler Effect

The change in the frequency of sound that occurs when either the source or the observer is moving can be written down explicitly. If the source is moving, we obtain

$$f = f_o \left(\frac{1}{1 \mp \dfrac{v_s}{v}} \right)$$

where f_o is the frequency when the source is not moving, f is the new frequency, v is the speed of sound, and v_s is the speed of the source. If the source is moving toward the observer, we use the minus sign. This must be the case to shift the frequency to a higher value as observed experimentally. On the other hand, we use the plus sign when the source is moving away from the observer.

If the source is stationary and the observer is moving, we use a similar expression.

$$f = f_o \left(1 \pm \frac{v_o}{v} \right)$$

where v_o is the speed of the observer. In this case, we choose the plus sign when the observer is moving toward the source to get the higher frequency. Likewise, we choose the minus sign when the observer is moving away from the source.

Finally, if both the source and the observer are moving, we can multiply the expressions within the parentheses to get the combined effect. The expression is simpler to write and to use if we multiply the numerator and denominator by v.

$$f = f_o \left(\frac{v \pm v_o}{v \mp v_s} \right)$$

where the upper signs are used for motions of the source and receiver toward each other. The choice of signs is easy to remember if you remind yourself that motion toward each other produces a higher frequency.

15 Sound and Music

Example 15.6.1

A train whistle has a frequency $f_o = 200$ Hz when it is at rest relative to an observer. What is the frequency heard by an observer at rest if the train is traveling toward the observer at 20 m/s? Assume that the speed of sound is 343 m/s on this day.

$$f = f_o \left(\frac{1}{1 \mp \dfrac{v_s}{v}} \right) = (200 \, Hz) \left(\frac{1}{1 - \dfrac{20 \, m/s}{343 \, m/s}} \right) = 212.4 \, Hz$$

What if the train is standing still and the observer approaches the train at 20 m/s?

$$f = f_o \left(1 \pm \frac{v_o}{v} \right) = (200 \, Hz) \left(1 + \frac{20 \, m/s}{343 \, m/s} \right) = 211.7 \, Hz$$

Notice that the new frequencies are not the same for the two cases. In fact, we kept an extra digit in each answer to show you this difference. The difference would be much more significant if the velocities were closer to the speed of sound.

What is the observed frequency if both the train and the observer are moving toward each other at 20 m/s?

$$f = f_o \left(\frac{v \pm v_o}{v \mp v_s} \right) = (200 \, Hz) \left(\frac{343 \, m/s + 20 \, m/s}{343 \, m/s - 20 \, m/s} \right) = 225 \, Hz$$

Practice

Show that you can get this last answer by using the frequency obtained in the first part of the problem as f_o in the second calculation.

◆ ◆ ◆

Problems

1. What is the speed of sound on a hot day when the temperature is 40°C?
2. How hot does it have to get for the speed of sound to be 350 m/s?

*3. If the speed of sound in iron is 5100 m/s, how much longer will it take sound to travel 1 km in air compared to 1 km in an iron rail?

*4. What is the time delay between signals traveling in air and water over a distance of 0.5 km?

*5. As you clap your hands at a frequency of 2 Hz, you back away from a wall until the echo reaches you just as you clap the next time. How far from the wall are you?

*6. You watch a carpenter driving nails at a regular rate of one blow per second. The sound of the blows is exactly synchronized with the blows you see. After the carpenter stops hammering, you hear two more blows. How far away is the carpenter?

7. What is the sound level for a whistle that has a sound intensity of 10^{-2} W/m^2?

8. What is the sound intensity in W/m^2 for an 80-dB sound?

9. What is the frequency of the note "C" located three octaves above "middle C" (f = 262 Hz)?

10. When a woman speaks with helium in her voice box, the frequency of her voice raises by a factor of three. Approximately how many octaves higher is her voice?

11. If the speed of the traveling waves on a 30-cm wire is 600 m/s, what is its fundamental frequency?

12. Waves travel at 500 m/s on a wire. If the wire is 75-cm long, what is the fundamental frequency of the wire?

13. If a guitar string has a length of 60 cm and a wave speed of 500 m/s, what are the wavelengths and frequencies of the first three harmonics?

14. If a guitar string has a length of 66 cm and a wave speed of 660 m/s, what are the wavelengths and frequencies of the first three harmonics?

15. What is the fundamental frequency of an open organ pipe with a length of 50 cm?

16. How long would an open organ pipe need to be to produce a frequency of 440 Hz?

17. What is the fundamental frequency of a closed organ pipe with a length of 50 cm?

18. How long would a closed organ pipe need to be to produce a frequency of 440 Hz?

19. What is the beat frequency produced by two sound waves with frequencies of 1048 Hz and 1052 Hz?

20. If two sound waves produce a beat frequency of 2 Hz and one of the waves has a frequency of 524 Hz, what is the frequency of the note you would hear?

21. A high-pitched whistle has a frequency of 600 Hz. What is the frequency heard by an observer at rest when the whistle is moving away from the observer at 30 m/s?

22. A stationary, high-pitched whistle has a frequency of 600 Hz. What is the frequency heard by an observer moving away from the whistle at 30 m/s?

23. A passenger in a high speed train hears a crossing bell with a frequency of 500 Hz (as heard by someone on the ground). If the train is traveling at 50 m/s, what is the shift in frequency heard by the passenger as the train passes the bell?

24. A commuter is standing on the train platform as the express train passes through at 30 m/s. If the train's whistle has a frequency of 300 Hz, what change in frequency does the commuter hear?

*25. A police car going 35 m/s is approaching you in a car traveling at 25 m/s. If the siren has a frequency of 400 Hz, what are the frequencies you hear while the police car approaches and after it has passed you?

*26. What frequencies would you hear if the police car in the previous problem overtook you from behind?

16 LIGHT

16.1 Pinhole Cameras

The size of the image produced by a pinhole camera depends on the object's size and the relative distances of the object and the image from the pinhole. In Fig. 16.1.1 two rays are drawn from the top and bottom of the object to the film plane. Since the two rays cross at the pinhole, we know that the angles formed at the crossing are equal, giving us two triangles that have the same shape. Such similar triangles have the property that the ratios of corresponding dimensions are equal. For our purposes, we equate the ratio of

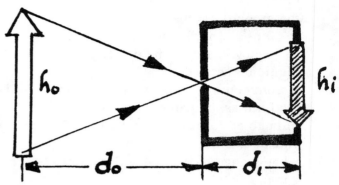

Fig. 16.1.1

the heights to the ratio of the bases. The heights are the object size h_o and image size h_i, while the bases are the distance d_i from the pinhole to the image and the distance d_o from the pinhole to the object. Symbolically, we have

$$\frac{h_i}{h_o} = \frac{d_i}{d_o}$$

Example 16.1.1

As an example, let's calculate the size of the image of a person who is 2 m tall if the person stands 4 m from the pinhole. Assume that the back wall of the pinhole camera is 0.4 m from the pinhole.

Solving our expression for the image height and plugging in numbers, we obtain

$$h_i = h_o \frac{d_i}{d_o} = (2\,m)\,\frac{0.4\,m}{4\,m} = 0.2\,m$$

Therefore, the image will be 0.2 m tall, which is 1/10th the size of the person.

Practice[1]

What is the image size if the person moves to 2 m from the pinhole?

---

[1] 0.4 m

16.2 Locating the Images

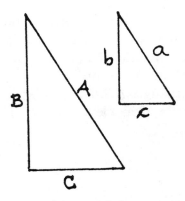

Although ray diagrams are very useful in determining what type of image is produced and roughly where the image is located, an algebraic equation will give us more accurate results. Using geometry and algebra, we can derive an expression for the magnification m and a relationship between the distance s of the object from the surface of the mirror, the distance s' of the image from the surface of the mirror, and the focal length f of the mirror.

Fig. 16.2.1

In our derivation, we will need to examine various *similar* triangles. These are triangles that have the same shape, but differ in size. We will only need to use similar right triangles. Two right triangles are similar if they have one other angle the same. In effect, this means that all three angles are the same. Corresponding dimensions of similar triangles are proportional to each other. If the corresponding sides are labeled as in Fig. 16.2.1, this can be written

$$\frac{a}{A} = \frac{b}{B} = \frac{c}{C}$$

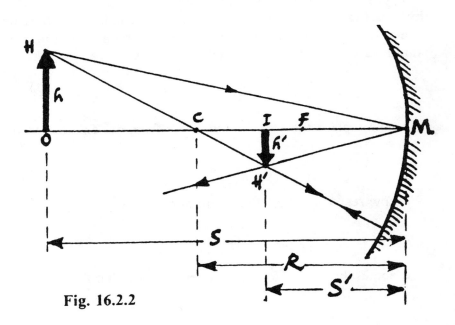

Fig. 16.2.2

In Fig. 16.2.2, we have drawn a ray diagram for locating the image I of an object O formed by a concave mirror with a focal length f. The ray from the top of the object (point H) to the intersection of the optic axis with the surface of the mirror (point M) is not one of our usual rays, but is useful in our derivation. We designate angles with three letters. For example, consider the ray *HM* that we just discussed. Its angle of incidence is the angle *HMO* since the optic axis in normal to the surface. The reflected angle is *IMH'*. Triangles are designated by the letters at the three corners.

The triangle *HOM* is similar to triangle *H'IM* since the angle of reflection *IMH'* is equal to the angle of incidence *HMO*. Therefore,

$$\frac{h'}{h} = \frac{s'}{s}$$

where h and h' are the heights of the object and image, respectively. But this ratio is just the magnification m.

$$m \equiv \frac{h'}{h} = \frac{-s'}{s}$$

where the minus sign is inserted to agree with the standard sign convention.

> m is positive if the image is erect
> m is negative if the image is inverted

To obtain the relationship for the image location, we use triangles *HOC* and *H'IC*. These triangles are similar because the angles at C are equal to each other because they are formed by crossing straight lines. Notice that the length of the horizontal side of triangle *HOC* is equal to $R - s'$ and the length of the horizontal side of triangle *H'IC* is $s - R$. Therefore, these similar triangles give us the following ratios.

$$\frac{h'}{h} = \frac{R - s'}{s - R}$$

We now replace the ratio h'/h with s'/s from our first set of similar triangles.

$$\frac{s'}{s} = \frac{R - s'}{s - R}$$

We now rearrange the latter expression to get

$$\frac{1}{s} + \frac{1}{s'} = \frac{2}{R}$$

We obtain the mirror formula by recognizing that $f = R/2$.

$$\frac{1}{s} + \frac{1}{s'} = \frac{1}{f}$$

The mirror formula can be used for concave and convex mirrors provided the sign convention for the focal lengths is used.

f is positive for a concave mirror
f is negative for a convex mirror

If we restrict ourselves to cases with a single mirror and real objects, the sign for the object distance s is always positive. The sign for the image distance s' tells us whether the image is located in front of or behind the mirror and whether it is real or virtual. Virtual images are located behind the mirror and real images are located in front of the mirror.

s' is positive if the image is in front of the mirror and real
s' is negative if the image is behind the mirror and virtual

Example 16.2.1

The focal length of a concave mirror is 20 cm. An object is located 60 cm in front of the mirror. Where is the image located? What type of image is it? What is the magnification of the image? Is it erect or inverted?

The mirror is concave, so the focal length is positive. Rearranging the mirror formula, we have

$$\frac{1}{s'} = \frac{1}{f} - \frac{1}{s} = \frac{1}{20\ cm} - \frac{1}{60\ cm} = \frac{3-1}{60\ cm} = \frac{2}{60\ cm} = \frac{1}{30\ cm}$$

$$s' = 30\ cm$$

Because s' is positive, the image is real and located in front of the mirror. We can now find the magnification.

$$m = -\frac{s'}{s} = -\frac{30\ cm}{60\ cm} = -\frac{1}{2}$$

The magnification is negative, which means that the image is inverted. The image is one-half as big as the object.

Practice[2]

Describe the image produced when this object is moved to 10 cm from the mirror.

Example 16.2.2

The focal length of a convex mirror is 20 cm. An object is located 20 cm in front of the mirror. Describe the image.

---

[2] $s' = -20$ cm (virtual image behind the mirror) and m = 2 (erect)

The focal length is negative for a convex mirror.

$$\frac{1}{s'} = \frac{1}{f} - \frac{1}{s} = \frac{1}{-20\ cm} - \frac{1}{20\ cm} = \frac{-2}{20\ cm} = \frac{-1}{10\ cm}$$

$$s' = -10\ cm$$

Since s' is negative, the image is virtual and located behind the mirror. The magnification is given by

$$m = -\frac{s'}{s} = -\frac{-10\ cm}{20\ cm} = \frac{1}{2}$$

The magnification is positive, so we know that the image is erect and one-half as big as the object.

Practice[3]

Describe the image produced when this object is moved to 10 cm from the mirror.

◆ ◆ ◆

16.3 Speed of Light

The distances in astronomy are often so large that they measure them in light years, the *distance* light travels in one year. Knowing the speed of light, we can calculate the length of a light year.

$$1\ LY = ct = (3 \times 10^8\ m/s)(1 year)\left(\frac{365.25\ days}{1\ year}\right)\left(\frac{24\ h}{1\ day}\right)\left(\frac{3600\ s}{1\ h}\right)$$

$$= 9.47 \times 10^{15}\ m$$

This is a tremendous distance, 9.47 trillion kilometers or almost 6 trillion miles!

Example 16.3.1

The Andromeda galaxy is located about 2.1×10^{19} km from earth. We are able to see it with our naked eyes because it shines with the light of more than 200 billion stars. What is the distance to the Andromeda galaxy measured in light years?

---

[3] $s' = $ -6.67 cm (virtual image behind the mirror) and m = 2/3 (erect)

$$d = 2.1 \times 10^{19} \, km \left(\frac{1 \, LY}{9.46 \times 10^{12} \, km} \right) = 2.2 \times 10^{6} \, LY$$

Since the Andromeda galaxy is 2.2 million light years away, we know that the light leaving there now will not arrive at earth for 2.2 million years.

Practice[4]

The brightest star that we observe in the night sky is Sirius. One of the reasons that it appears so bright is that it is relatively close to earth. If the distance to Sirius is 8.1×10^{13} km, how long does it take light from Sirius to reach us?

◆ ◆ ◆

Problems

1. A camera obscura used by a portrait painter is located 5 m from a child who stands 1 m tall. How big is her image if the back of the camera obscura is 2 m away?

2. A landscape painter places a camera obscura 40 m from a 12-m tall tree. How big is the image if the back wall is 2 m away from the pinhole?

3. An artist would like to paint a portrait that is one-fourth the size of the person. If the distance to the screen is 0.5 m from the pinhole, how far from the pinhole should the person stand?

4. What distance from the pinhole to the back wall of a camera obscura is needed to produce an image of the full moon that is 10 cm in diameter?

5. A concave mirror has a focal length of 30 cm. What kind of image is produced by an object located 60 cm from the mirror? Where is it located and what is its magnification?

6. A 15-cm ruler is placed 75 cm in front of a concave mirror with a focal length of 50 cm. Where is the image located and how big is it?

7. Where is the image located if an object is placed 10 cm away from a concave mirror with a focal length of 30 cm?

8. A 5-cm tall candle is placed 20 cm from a concave mirror that has a focal length of 50 cm. How big is the image and where is it located?

*9. Where is the image of a candle placed at the focal point of a concave mirror?

---

[4] 8.55 years

*10. Where in front of a concave mirror would you place a candle so that it appears to burn at both ends?

11. If your nose is 10 cm from the surface of a shiny metal sphere with a diameter of 6 cm, where is the image of your nose?

12. The right side mirror on a truck has a focal length of 2 m. A car is located 5 m from the mirror. How much closer is the image of the car than the car itself?

*13. Show that a convex mirror cannot produce a real image of an object.

*14. Where would you place an object in front of a convex mirror so that its image is one-half the size of the object.

15. The star Aldebaran, the red eye of Taurus, the Bull, is 4.9×10^{14} km from earth. How long does it take its light to reach earth?

16. If all of the stars were somehow placed at the same distance from the sun, the star Rigel in Orion would be the brightest star in the heavens. It appears dimmer than other stars because it is about 7.7×10^{15} km away. If Rigel suddenly blew apart, how long would it be before we would know about it?

17. If the diameter of the Milky Way Galaxy is 100,000 LY, how far is it across in km?

18. If light from a quasar takes 8 billion years to reach earth, how far away is the quasar in km?

19. Supernova 1987A occurred at a distance of 1.6×10^{18} km from earth. How far long ago did it occur?

20. Light from the time the universe became transparent after the Big Bang has been traveling for 10-20 billion years. How big is the observable universe as seen from earth?

17 REFRACTION OF LIGHT

17.1 Refraction and Observing

If you measure the depth of the image produced in the water in Fig. 17-4(c) in the text, you will discover that the image depth is three-fourths the depth of the object. It is interesting to note that the index of refraction of water is four-thirds, that is, it is the reciprocal of the relative depth. Similar drawings for other substances such as glass verify that the depth d' of the image is given by

$$d' = \frac{d}{n}$$

where d is the depth of the object and n is the index of refraction.

Example 17.1.1

A decal is pasted on the far side of a thick piece of glass. If the glass in 6 cm thick, how far into the glass does the image of the decal appear?

The index of refraction for the glass that we used in the text is 1.5, therefore

$$d' = \frac{d}{n} = \frac{6\ cm}{1.5} = 4\ cm$$

Practice[1]

Where is the image if the glass has an index of refraction equal to 2?

◆ ◆ ◆

17.2 Images Produced by Lenses

Although ray diagrams are very useful in determining what type of image is produced and roughly where the image is located, algebraic equations give us more accurate results. Using geometry and algebra, we can show that the formulas that we used for mirrors in Section 16.2 can also be used for lens with minor changes in definition. We let s be the distance from the object to the center of the lens, s' be the distance of the image from the center of the lens, and the f be the focal length of the lens as shown in Fig. 17.2.1.

---

[1] 3 cm

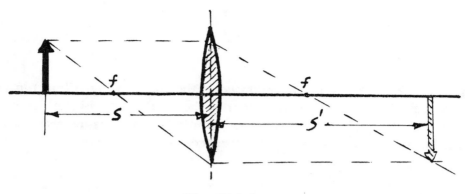

Fig. 17.2.1

The lens formula is identical to the mirror formula

$$\frac{1}{s} + \frac{1}{s'} = \frac{1}{f}$$

with following conventions for the focal length.

> f is positive for a converging lens
> f is negative for a diverging lens

Once again the sign of the image distance tells us the location of the image and whether it is real or virtual. If the object is located on the near side of the lens, images on the far side are real and images on the near side are virtual.

> s' is positive if the image is on the far side of the lens and real
> s' is negative if the image is on the near side of the lens and virtual

We can also use the same equation for the magnification of the image

$$m = -\frac{s'}{s}$$

with the sign convention that

> m is positive if the image is erect
> m is negative if the image is inverted

Example 17.2.1

> The focal length of a converging lens is 20 cm. An object is located 60 cm from the lens. Where is the image located? What type of image is it? What is the magnification of the image? Is it erect or inverted?

Since the lens is converging, the focal length is positive. Rearranging the lens formula, we have

$$\frac{1}{s'} = \frac{1}{f} - \frac{1}{s} = \frac{1}{20\ cm} - \frac{1}{60\ cm} = \frac{3-1}{60\ cm} = \frac{2}{60\ cm} = \frac{1}{30\ cm}$$

$$s' = 30\ cm$$

s' is positive, indicating that the image is real. It is located 30 cm from the lens on the far side (opposite the object). The magnification is

$$m = -\frac{s'}{s} = -\frac{30\ cm}{60\ cm} = -\frac{1}{2}$$

We know that the image is inverted because the magnification is negative. The image is one-half as big as the object.

Practice[2]

Describe the image produced when this object is moved to 10 cm from the lens.

Example 17.2.2

The focal length of a diverging lens is 20 cm. An object is located 20 cm from the lens. Describe the image.

The focal length is negative for a diverging lens.

$$\frac{1}{s'} = \frac{1}{f} - \frac{1}{s} = \frac{1}{-20\ cm} - \frac{1}{20\ cm} = \frac{-2}{20\ cm} = \frac{-1}{10\ cm}$$

$$s' = -10\ cm$$

Therefore, the image is virtual and located 10 cm from the lens on the near side with a magnification of

$$m = -\frac{s'}{s} = -\frac{-10\ cm}{20\ cm} = \frac{1}{2}$$

The positive magnification tells us that the image is erect.

---

[2] $s' = -20$ cm (virtual image on the near side) and m = 2 (erect)

Practice[3]

Describe the image produced when this object is moved to 10 cm from the lens.

◆ ◆ ◆

17.3 Cameras

Example 17.3.1

A camera with a 50-mm lens is used to take a portrait of a basketball player with a height of 2 m. If the player stands 2 m from the lens, where is the image formed and how large will it be?

Setting $f = 5$ cm and $s = 200$ cm, we calculate the image location s' to be

$$\frac{1}{s'} = \frac{1}{f} - \frac{1}{s} = \frac{1}{5\ cm} - \frac{1}{200\ cm} = \frac{39}{200\ cm}$$

$$s' = \frac{200\ cm}{39} = 5.13\ cm = 51.3\ mm$$

Therefore, the lens should be adjusted to be 51.3 mm from the film. Notice that this is very close to the focal length of the lens. As the subject moves farther away, the term $1/s$ approaches zero and the image distance approaches the focal length. Therefore, for objects at infinity, the film should be located at the focal point.

We can calculate the image size using the magnification.

$$h' = h\ \frac{(-s')}{s} = (2\ m)\ \frac{(-51.3\ mm)}{2\ m} = -51.3\ mm$$

Since the film is only 35-mm wide, you cannot take a full view without turning the camera on its side. However, if you switch to a wide angle lens with a 28-mm focal length, the image will fit.

Practice[4]

What is the image size using the 28-mm lens?

◆ ◆ ◆

---

[3] $s' = $ -6.67 cm (virtual image on the near side of the lens) and m = 0.667 (erect)

[4] 28.4 mm high

17.4 Our Eyes

Example 17.4.1

What is the focal length of a lens rated at +64 diopters?

$$f = \frac{1\,m}{d} = \frac{1\,m}{64} = 0.0156\,m = 1.56\,cm$$

Example 17.4.2

If your eyeball is 1.67 cm long, how close must an object be to form a focused image on the retina when the lens in the eye has the maximum 64 diopters?

Setting $s' = 1.67$ cm and using the focal length from the previous example, we have

$$\frac{1}{s} = \frac{1}{f} - \frac{1}{s'} = \frac{1}{1.56\,cm} - \frac{1}{1.67\,cm} = 0.0422/cm$$

$$s = 23.7\,cm$$

◆ ◆ ◆

17.5 Magnifiers

Your eyes are not able to focus on objects closer than the *near point* of your eyes. This puts a limit on the angular size of the object. If you bring it closer to increase the size of its image on your retina, the image becomes blurred. However, if you place a converging lens so that the object is at its focal point, the lens produces an image at infinity that is easy to look at. Moreover the image on your retina is bigger. If the near point for your eyes is d_n, the magnification of the simple magnifier is given by

$$m = \frac{d_n}{f}$$

where f is the focal length of the lens.

Example 17.5.1

If your near point is 24 cm and the magnifying glass has a focal length of 6 cm, what is the magnification?

$$m = \frac{d_n}{f} = \frac{24\ cm}{6\ cm} = 4$$

This is the largest practical magnification that you can get with a single lens. Large magnifications can be obtained by using combinations of lens to correct for distortions.

◆ ◆ ◆

Problems

1. Where is the image of a decal on the bottom of an 8-ft deep swimming pool?

2. If a rare stamp is kept under 2 cm of glass, how close to the top surface is its image?

3. A fish is swimming behind a thick glass window (n = 1.5) used as a viewing port into an aquarium. If the fish is next to the window and the window is 4 cm thick, how far behind the front of the window does the fish appear to be?

*4. A swimmer lying on the bottom of a swimming pool observes a light on the ceiling. If the ceiling is 8-ft tall, how far above the water does the light appear to be?

5. A converging lens has a focal length of 30 cm. What kind of image is produced by an object located 60 cm from the lens? Where is the image located and what is its magnification?

6. A 15-cm ruler is placed 75 cm from a converging lens with a focal length of 50 cm. Where is the image located and how big is it?

7. Where is the image if an object is placed 10 cm from a converging lens with a focal length of 30 cm?

8. A 5-cm tall candle is placed 20 cm from a converging lens that has a focal length of 50 cm. How big is the image and where is it located?

9. A converging lens with a focal length of 20 cm is used to make a slide projector. If the image is to be projected onto a screen 10 m away, how far from the lens should the slide be placed?

10. An overhead projector is made from a converging lens with a focal length of 60 cm. If the image is projected onto a screen at a distance of 4 m, how far should the lens be from the transparency?

11. If your nose is 10 cm from a diverging lens with a focal length of 5 cm, where is the image of your nose?

12. A diverging lens with a focal length of 40 cm is placed 60 cm from a 4-cm tall candle. Where is the image of the candle and how big is it?

13. A diverging lens has a focal length of 30 cm. What kind of image is produced by an object located 20 cm from the lens? Where is the image located and what is its magnification?

14.   Where is the image located if an object is placed 10 cm away from a diverging lens with a focal length of 30 cm?

15.   A tourist in Yellowstone National Park takes a photograph of a buffalo that is 40 m away and 1.5 m tall. If the lens has a focal length of 50-mm, how large is the image of the buffalo on the film?

16.   If the tourist in the previous problem switches to a telephoto lens with a focal length of 200 mm, how large will the image of the buffalo be?

17.   What is the size of the image on the retina if a person is looking at a cowboy who is 3 m away and stands 180 cm tall?

18.   A person is looking at a house that is 12 m tall to the top of the roof. If the person is 50 m away, how tall is the image on the retina?

19.   A converging lens rated at +6 diopters is bonded to a diverging lens of -4 diopters. What is the focal length of the combination?

20.   If a converging lens (+3 diopters) and a diverging lens (-6 diopters) are glued together, what is the focal length of the pair?

21.   A 10-year-old child can focus as close as 7 cm. What focal length lens should the child use to get a magnification of 4?

22.   A senior citizen has a near point that is 200 cm. What focal length lens should the senior citizen use to get a magnification of 4?

18   A MODEL FOR LIGHT

18.1 Speed of Light in Materials

As discussed in the text, the speed of light in materials is slower than the speed in a vacuum. Michelson showed that the speed v in a material is given by

$$v = \frac{c}{n}$$

where c is the speed in a vacuum and n is the index of refraction of the material.

Example 18.1.1

What is the speed of light in diamond with an index of refraction of 2.42?

$$v = \frac{c}{n} = \frac{3 \times 10^8 \, m/s}{2.42} = 1.24 \times 10^8 \, m/s$$

Practice[1]

What is the speed of light in zircon (fake diamond) with an index of 1.92?

◆ ◆ ◆

18.2 Interference

The equation that we used for the interference of water waves in Sec. 14.9 holds for all types of waves. Therefore, we can use the equation with light.

$$y_{max} = m \frac{\lambda L}{d} \qquad m = 0, \pm 1, \pm 2, \pm 3, \ldots$$

where y_{max} is the distance measured along the wall from the central bright region to another bright (antinodal) region, λ is the wavelength, L is the distance to the wall, d is the spacing of the slits, and m is an integer that numbers the antinodal regions.

Example 18.2.1

The light from a helium-neon laser has a wavelength of 633 nm. If the laser beam shines on two narrow slits separated by 0.1 mm, what is the spacing of the interference antinodes on a wall 10 m away?

---

[1] 1.56×10^8 m/s

Since we know that $y_{max} = 0$ for m = 0, we can calculate the location of the first maximum (m = 1) to find the spacing. Being careful to express the lengths in meters (or at least units that will cancel), we have

$$y_{max} = m \frac{\lambda L}{d} = (1) \frac{(6.33 \times 10^{-7} \, m)(10 \, m)}{1 \times 10^{-4} \, m} = 6.33 \times 10^{-2} \, m$$

Therefore, the bright regions will be 6.33 cm apart on the wall.

Practice[2]

What is the spacing on the wall if light from a sodium vapor lamp ($\lambda = 589$ nm) is used?

Example 18.2.2

The spacing of the bright lines in an interference pattern is measured to be 2.2 cm. If the wall is 1.5 m away from slits with a spacing of 0.05 mm, what is the wavelength of the light?

$$\lambda = \frac{y_{max} d}{mL} = \frac{(2.2 \times 10^{-2} \, m)(5 \times 10^{-5} \, m)}{(1)(1.5 \, m)} = 733 \, nm$$

◆ ◆ ◆

18.3 Diffraction

We can also use our expression for the diffraction pattern from Sec. 14.10 to analyze the diffraction of light.

$$y_{min} = m \frac{\lambda L}{w} \qquad\qquad m = \pm 1, \pm 2, \pm 3, \ldots$$

where y_{max} is the distance measured along the wall from the central bright region, λ is the wavelength to the nodal regions, L is the distance to the wall, d is the spacing of the slits, and m is an integer that numbers the nodal regions. Notice that m = 0 is excluded. This occurs because the central region is an antinodal region. This central region is twice as wide as the other antinodal regions and is much brighter than those on either side.

---

[2] 5.89 cm apart

Example 18.3.1

How wide is the central maximum produced by yellow light with a wavelength of 600 nm striking a slit with a width of 0.09 mm if the slit is 180 cm from the viewing screen?

We know that the minima on either side of the central maximum are given by our formula. Therefore, the full width of the maximum is given by the difference in y_{min} with m = 1 and m = -1. For m = 1, we have

$$y_{min} = m \frac{\lambda L}{w} = (1) \frac{(6 \times 10^{-7} \, m)(180 \, cm)}{0.009 \, cm} = 1.2 \times 10^{-2} \, m$$

Therefore, one minimum is at 1.2 cm. The minimum on the other side must be at -1.2 cm. This gives a full width of 2.4 cm for the central maximum.

Practice[3]

What happens to the width of the central maximum if the screen is moved twice as far away?

◆ ◆ ◆

18.4 Thin Films

When light shines on a thin film in air, the waves that reflect from the front surface are inverted, while those reflecting from the back surface are not inverted (Fig. 18-10 in the text). This means that a very thin film (much thinner than the wavelength of the light) will not reflect light because the two reflected waves will interfere destructively.

If the thickness of the film is increased to equal one-fourth of the wavelength of the light measured *in the film*, the waves reflecting off the back surface travel an extra one-half wavelength and emerge in phase with those reflected from the front surface. This means that the light will be strongly reflected. Every time the thickness of the film is increased by an additional half wavelength, the wave inside the film travels an extra wavelength and continues to emerge in phase. The following thicknesses will yield strong reflections.

$$d_m = \frac{\lambda_f}{4} + m \frac{\lambda_f}{2} = (m + \frac{1}{2}) \frac{\lambda_f}{2} \qquad \text{for } m = 0, 1, 2, 3, \ldots$$

where λ_f is the wavelength in the film

---

[3] It doubles to 4.8 cm.

$$\lambda_f = \frac{\lambda}{n}$$

with λ the wavelength in a vacuum and n the index of refraction of the film.

If a film is coated onto a material with a higher index of refraction, the waves are not inverted at the back surface. In this case, a film with "zero" thickness would reflect light strongly. Increases in the thickness of one-half wavelength would also produce strong reflection. Therefore, the possible thicknesses for strong reflections are

$$d_m = m\frac{\lambda_f}{2} \qquad for \ m = 1, 2, 3, \ldots$$

Example 18.4.1

What thicknesses of a soap film will strongly reflect light from a helium-neon laser with a wavelength of 633 nm in air?

If we assume that the index of a soap film is close to that of water, the wavelength of the light in the film is

$$\lambda_f = \frac{\lambda}{n} = \frac{633 \, nm}{1.33} = 476 \, nm$$

Since the soap film is in air, we use our first equation to calculate the thicknesses.

$$d_m = (m + \frac{1}{2})\frac{\lambda_f}{2} = (m + \frac{1}{2})\frac{476 \, nm}{2} = (m + \frac{1}{2})(238 \, nm)$$

$$d_0 = \frac{1}{2}(238 \, nm) = 119 \, nm$$

$$d_1 = \frac{3}{2}(238 \, nm) = 357 \, nm$$

$$d_2 = \frac{5}{2}(238 \, nm) = 595 \, nm$$

and so on.

Practice[4]

What is the thinnest soap film that will strongly reflect green light with a wavelength of 550 nm?

---

[4] 103 nm

Example 18.4.2

A camera lens is coated with a thin film of magnesium fluoride with an index of refraction of 1.38. What thickness should be used to reflect violet light with a wavelength of 414 nm?

Because the film has an index of refraction that is intermediate between the air and the glass, inversions will take place at both surfaces of the film. Therefore, we use our second equation to obtain the desired thickness.

$$d_m = m\frac{\lambda_f}{2} = (1)\frac{\lambda}{2n} = \frac{414\,nm}{2(1.38)} = 150\,nm$$

Practice[5]

What is the next thickness that will strongly reflect this light?

◆ ◆ ◆

Problems

1. What is the speed of light in ice (index of refraction = 1.31)?

2. What is the speed of light in carbon tetrachloride which has an index of refraction of 1.46?

3. What is the index of refraction of a substance in which the speed of light is measured to be 2×10^8 m/s?

4. If it takes light 2 ns to traverse 40 cm of glass, what is the index of refraction of the glass?

5. By how much is light delayed in traveling through 3 m of glass (n = 1.5) compared to a vacuum?

*6. If light ($\lambda = 633$ nm) travels through 1 mm of glass (n = 1.5), by how many wavelengths will it be delayed compared to a vacuum?

7. Green light from a mercury discharge tube ($\lambda = 546$ nm) shines on two slits separated by 0.25 mm. What is the location of the second maximum on a screen 80 cm away?

8. Blue-green light from an argon laser ($\lambda = 515$ nm) produces an interference pattern on a screen located 1.2 m from two slits with a separation of 0.3 mm. What is the spacing of the pattern?

9. In a double slit interference experiment, the third maximum is located 4.8 cm from the central maximum. If the screen is located 2 m from the slits and the slits have a separation of 0.07 mm, what is the wavelength of the light?

---

[5] 300 nm

10. The red light from a hydrogen discharge tube produces an interference pattern in which the third maximum is 3.5 cm from the central maximum. If the screen is 0.75 m away and the wavelength is 656 nm, what is the spacing of the slits?

11. What is the width of the central maximum of the diffraction pattern produced by light with a wavelength of 600 nm shining on a slit (w = 0.05 mm) if the viewing screen is 1.4 m away?

12. A 0.1-mm slit is illuminated with yellow light (λ = 588 nm) from a helium discharge tube. If the screen is 0.5 m away, what is the width of the central maximum?

13. The red light from a hydrogen discharge tube with a wavelength of 656 nm produces a diffraction pattern with a central maximum that is 1.5 cm wide. If the screen is 0.5 m away, what is the width of the slit?

14. Blue-green light from an argon laser (λ = 515 nm) produces a diffraction pattern on a screen located 1.5 m from a slit with a width of 0.3 mm. What is the spacing of the pattern?

15. What is the thinnest soap film that will strongly reflect yellow light with a wavelength of 589 nm?

*16. What is the thinnest soap film (other than zero) that will strongly transmit light with a wavelength of 589 nm?

17. What are the possible thicknesses of an oil layer on water that will strongly reflect green light of wavelength 520 nm in air? The index of refraction for oil is 1.3.

18. A camera lens is coated with a thin film of magnesium fluoride (index = 1.38) to minimize the reflection of yellow light with a wavelength of 600 nm in air. How thick is the film?

*19. A camera lens is coated with a 500-nm film of magnesium fluoride with an index of refraction of 1.38. What wavelengths in the visible range have minimal reflections?

19 ELECTRICITY

19.1 The Electric Force

Calculating an electric force is just a matter of plugging the given values into Coulomb's law. However, the ratio of two electric forces can often be obtained without knowing the values of the variables providing you know the relative values. Let's write down Coulomb's law for the original value of the force using the subscript o on each variable. Then the original force F_o is given by

$$F_o = k\,\frac{Q_o q_o}{r_o^2}$$

where the two charges Q_o and q_o are separated by a distance r_o.

If we write down the same expression for the new force in terms of the new charges and the new distance of separation using the subscript n, we have

$$F_n = k\,\frac{Q_n q_n}{r_n^2}$$

Taking the ratio of the two equations and canceling the common factor k, we obtain

$$\frac{F_n}{F_o} = \frac{Q_n q_n r_o^2}{Q_o q_o r_n^2}$$

Whenever a new value is the same as the old value, it can be canceled in the ratio on the right-hand side. If we then express the other new values in terms of the old values, we can obtain the ratio of the two forces.

Example 19.1.1

What happens to the force if the distance between two charged objects is tripled?

Assuming that the charges stay the same, that is, $Q_n = q_o$ and $q_n = q_o$, we can cancel them. Tripling the distance is the same as setting $r_n = 3r_o$. Therefore,

$$\frac{F_n}{F_o} = \frac{Q_n q_n r_o^2}{Q_o q_o r_n^2} = \frac{r_o^2}{r_n^2} = \frac{r_o^2}{(3r_o)^2} = \frac{1}{9}$$

Therefore, the new force has one-ninth the value of the old force.

What happens to the force if the size of each charge is doubled and their signs are reversed?

This means that $Q_n = -2Q_o$ and $q_n = -2q_o$. Therefore,

$$\frac{F_n}{F_o} = \frac{Q_n q_n r_o^2}{Q_o q_o r_n^2} = \frac{Q_n q_n}{Q_o q_o} = \frac{(-2Q_o)(-2q_o)}{Q_o q_o} = 4$$

Notice that the sign changes didn't change the direction of the force.

Practice[1]

What happens to the force if the charges and the separation are all doubled?

◆ ◆ ◆

19.2 Electricity and Gravity

In the text we calculated the gravitational and electric forces between an electron and a proton separated by a specified distance. Then we took the ratio of the two forces to show that the electric force was approximately 10^{39} times larger. An alternate way of calculating the ratio is to use the technique from the previous section. Writing the ratio symbolically, we have

$$\frac{F_e}{F_g} = \frac{kQ_1 Q_2}{GM_1 M_2}$$

where the distance of separation r cancels because it is the same for both forces.

Example 19.2.1

What is the ratio of the electric force between an electron and a proton to the gravitational force between them?

$$\frac{F_e}{F_g} = \frac{kQ_1 Q_2}{GM_1 M_2}$$

---

[1] The force stays the same.

$$\frac{F_e}{F_g} = \frac{(8.99 \times 10^9 \, \frac{N \cdot m^2}{C^2})(1.6 \times 10^{-19} \, C)^2}{(6.67 \times 10^{-11} \, \frac{N \cdot m^2}{kg^2})(9.11 \times 10^{-31} \, kg)(1.67 \times 10^{-27} \, kg)}$$

$$= 2.27 \times 10^{39}$$

which agrees with the answer in the text.

◆ ◆ ◆

19.3 The Electric Field

By definition, the electric field at a point in space is equal to the force on a unit positive charge placed at that point. In simple cases it can be obtained by calculating the force on a charge q and then dividing by q.

$$E = \frac{F}{q} = \frac{1}{q} k \frac{Qq}{r^2} = k \frac{Q}{r^2}$$

We see that the value of the electric field is independent of the value of the test charge q.

Example 19.3.1

What is the electric field at a distance of 10 cm from a point charge of 4 µC?

$$E = k \frac{Q}{r^2} = \left(8.99 \times 10^9 \, \frac{N \cdot m^2}{C^2}\right) \frac{4 \times 10^{-6} \, C}{(0.10 \, m)^2} = 3.6 \times 10^6 \, \frac{N}{C}$$

Because the electric field is a vector, we must give its direction to completely specify it. The field points directly away from a positive charge because that is the direction of the force on a positive charge placed at the field point.

If a charge of -5 µC is placed at this point, what force will it experience?

Since $E = F/q$, we have $F = qE$. Therefore,

$$F = qE = (-5 \times 10^{-6} \, C)(3.6 \times 10^6 \, \frac{N}{C}) = -18 \, N$$

The minus sign means that the force is in the direction opposite the field, that is, directed toward the original charge. This makes sense because the two charges have opposite signs and they will attract each other.

Practice[2]

What is the electric field 20 cm from a point charge of -20 μC?

◆ ◆ ◆

19.4 Electric Potential

Example 19.4.1

If it requires 10 J of work to take an object with a charge of 2 C between points A and B, what is the electric potential difference between A and B?

$$\Delta V = \frac{W}{q} = \frac{10\,J}{2\,C} = 5\,\frac{J}{C} = 5\,V$$

In the last step we replaced the combination J/C by volts V.

We can now calculate the work required to take <u>any</u> charge between A and B. For instance, 4 C would require

$$W = q\,\Delta V = (4\,C)(5\,V) = 20\,J$$

Practice[3]

What would the potential difference be if it required 10 J of work to take a charge of -2 C between A and B?

◆ ◆ ◆

Problems

1. A nucleus contains 92 protons and 143 neutrons. What electric force does this nucleus exert on a single electron that is orbiting the nucleus at a distance of 0.1 nm?

2. If an atom has a diameter of 0.3 nm. What is the electric force between two electrons on opposite sides of the atom?

---

[2] 4.5 x 10^6 N/C toward the charge.

[3] -5 V

3. Equal charges of 2 C are placed at the corners of a right triangle whose short sides are each 1 m long. What is the net force on the charge at the right angle?

4. Equal charges of 3 C are placed at the corners of a square with sides 2 m long. What is the net force on each charge?

5. What is the electric force between two protons separated by 5×10^{-11} m? How does this compare to that between an electron and a proton separated by the same distance?

6. What is the electric force between two electrons separated by 1 m?

7. Two charged objects are very, very far from any other charges. If the distance between them is cut in half, what happens to the electrical force between them?

8. Assume that you have two identically charged objects separated by a certain distance. How would the force change if the objects were three times as far away from each other?

9. Assume that you have two identically charged objects separated by a certain distance. How would the force change if one object had twice the charge and the other object kept the same charge?

10. Two charged objects are very, very far from any other charges. If the charge on both of them is quadrupled, what happens to the electric force between them?

11. What is the acceleration of an electron at a distance of 2 m from a charge of +3 C?

12. What is the centripetal acceleration of an electron orbiting a proton at a distance of 0.05 nm?

*13. Show that the earth and moon would each need an electric charge of about 10^{14} C to have an electric force between them equal to their gravitational attraction.

*14. What equal charges would be needed for two 80-kg people to have the same electric repulsion as their gravitational attraction?

15. Calculate the electric field at a distance of 6 m from 5 C of negative charge.

16. What is the acceleration of an electron in a uniform electric field of 2×10^4 N/C?

*17. What is the acceleration of an electron located 10^{-12} m from a fixed proton?

*18. A small ball has a charge of 1 mC and a mass of 100 g. What electric field would be needed to keep the ball suspended in the air?

19. It requires 25 J of work to move a charged object between two locations. If the electric potential energy of the object was originally 50 J, what is its potential energy at the new location?

20. It requires 25 J of work to move a charged object between two locations that have an electric potential difference of 250 V. What is the charge on the object?

21. A 9-V battery does 36 J of work in pushing 4 C of charge through a circuit containing one light bulb. How much work is done by the same battery when it moves the same

amount of charge through a circuit containing two bulbs in series?

22. Points A and C each have an electric potential of +6 V and point B has an electric potential of +12 V. How much work is required to take 2 C of charge from A to B to C?

23. Points A and B have electrical potentials of 6 V and 12 V, respectively. How much work would be required to take 3 C of positive charge from A to B? How much work would it take for 3 C of negative charge?

24. How much work does a 12-V battery do when one electron moves from the negative terminal to the positive terminal?

25. If a spark jumps across a gap of 0.2 cm, what is the minimum electric potential difference across the gap?

26. If an electrostatic generator produces a electric potential of 1 million volts, what is the minimum distance it must be placed from surrounding materials to prevent sparking?

27. Show that the units (CV) used in conjunction with the work performed by a battery are the same as those (J) we used in Chapter 6.

*28. Show that the units (V/m) used in describing the electric fields required for sparks and lightning are equivalent to those (N/C) used in the defining equation.

20   ELECTRIC CHARGES IN MOTION

20.1 Resistance

We learned in the text that the resistance of a piece of wire depends on the type of wire, increases as the wire gets longer, and decreases as the wire is made bigger in diameter. These qualitative statements can be made quantitative by conducting measurements on different wires. The conclusions can be expressed by

$$R = \rho \frac{L}{A}$$

where R is the resistance, ρ is the **resistivity** of the material, L is the length, and A is the cross-sectional area of the wire. For a circular wire the cross-sectional area is given by $A = \pi r^2$.

The resistivity is a measure of the difficulty for an electric current to flow through a standard-sized piece of the material. The smaller the number, the larger the current for the same voltage. The resistivity is numerically equal to the resistance of a piece of the material that is 1 m long and 1 m^2 in cross-section. The units of resistivity are ohm-meter ($\Omega \cdot m$) as can be seen from the equation above. The values of the resistivities of some common materials are given in Table 20.1.1.

Table 20.1.1 Resistivities of Some Common Materials

Material	Resistivity ($\Omega \cdot m$)
Silver	1.59×10^{-8}
Copper	1.70×10^{-8}
Gold	2.44×10^{-8}
Aluminum	2.82×10^{-8}
Tungsten	5.6×10^{-8}
Nichrome	1.50×10^{-6}
Carbon	3.5×10^{-5}
Glass	$10^{10} - 10^{14}$
Hard Rubber	about 10^{13}
Amber	5×10^{14}

Example 20.1.1

What is the resistance of a piece of copper wire that has a diameter of 2 mm and a length of 5 m?

The cross-sectional area of the wire is given by

$$A = \pi r^2 = (3.14)(1 \times 10^{-3}\, m)^2 = 3.14 \times 10^{-6}\, m^2$$

The resistance is then

$$R = \rho\, \frac{L}{A} = (1.7 \times 10^{-8}\, \Omega \cdot m)\, \frac{5\, m}{3.14 \times 10^{-6}\, m^2} = 0.027\, \Omega$$

Practice[1]

What is the resistance of a tungsten wire used as the filament of a light bulb if it has a cross-sectional area of 10^{-9} m^2 and a length of 0.1 m?

◆ ◆ ◆

As shown in the previous examples and practice exercises, the resistances of the wires connecting light bulbs and other appliances are very much less than the resistances of the appliances. This means that one usually ignores the connecting wires when discussing resistance of a typical circuit.

We can now calculate the total resistance of individual resistances connected in series or parallel. Series is the easiest since this is just like putting two wires end to end. Since resistance depends on the length of wire, it is the total length that matters; resistances in series add.

$$R_t = R_1 + R_2 \qquad\qquad \textit{resistances in series add}$$

where R_t is the total resistance and R_1 and R_2 are the individual resistances.

The rule for obtaining the total resistance of two resistors in parallel is a bit harder. We start by realizing that two wires in parallel means more area, which in turn means an increase in the current. Let's look at the special case of two wires of equal length L. A simple assumption is that the combined resistance depends on the sum of the two areas.

$$A_t = A_1 + A_2$$

Using our resistivity equation, we can substitute for each area to obtain

$$\frac{\rho L}{R_t} = \frac{\rho L}{R_1} + \frac{\rho L}{R_2}$$

Canceling the common factor of ρL, we get

---

[1] 5.6 Ω

$$\frac{1}{R_t} = \frac{1}{R_1} + \frac{1}{R_2}$$

resistances in parallel add as reciprocals

Although this equation was obtained for a specific case of two wires of the same material and length, it actually holds for all resistances in parallel.

Example 20.1.2

What are the total resistances of a 4-Ω resistor and a 12-Ω resistor connected in series and parallel?

When they are connected in series, we have

$$R_t = R_1 + R_2 = 4\,\Omega + 12\,\Omega = 16\,\Omega$$

If we now connect them in parallel,

$$\frac{1}{R_t} = \frac{1}{R_1} + \frac{1}{R_2} = \frac{1}{4\,\Omega} + \frac{1}{12\,\Omega} = \frac{3}{12\,\Omega} + \frac{1}{12\,\Omega} = \frac{4}{12\,\Omega}$$

$$R_t = 3\,\Omega$$

Note that the total resistance of a parallel arrangement is less than either of the resistances alone. This is always true and makes sense because the second pathway will always make it easier for the electric charge to flow. No matter how large the second resistor, its addition into the circuit will always allow more charge to flow in a given amount of time.

Practice[2]

What are the resistances of 2 Ω and 10 Ω connected in series and in parallel?

◆ ◆ ◆

20.2 Ohm's Law

Example 20.2.1

A 12-Ω resistor and a 4-Ω resistor in series are connected to a 12-V battery. What is the current in the circuit and the voltage drop across each resistor?

---

[2] 12 Ω in series and 1.67 Ω in parallel

Because resistances in series add, the battery sees a total resistance of 16 Ω. The current in the circuit is then calculated from Ohm's law.

$$I = \frac{V}{R} = \frac{12\,V}{16\,\Omega} = \frac{3}{4}A$$

Because this current must flow through each resistor, we can apply Ohm's law to each resistor to find the voltage drop across it.

$$V_1 = IR_1 = \left(\frac{3}{4}A\right)(12\,\Omega) = 9\,V$$

$$V_2 = IR_2 = \left(\frac{3}{4}A\right)(4\,\Omega) = 3\,V$$

As a check, notice that the total voltage drop is just 9 V + 3 V = 12 V.

Practice[3]

    If the two resistors are connected in parallel, what is the current through each?

◆ ◆ ◆

20.3 Batteries and Bulbs

Ohm's law provides us with an alternate method for obtaining the rules for combining resistances. To see this, let's start with two resistors R_1 and R_2 connected in series as shown in Fig. 20.3.1. Conservation of energy requires that the voltage drop V_t across the pair be equal to the sum of the voltage drop V_1 across the first resistor and the voltage drop V_2 across the second resistor.

Fig. 20.3.1

$$V_t = V_1 + V_2$$

We can now use Ohm's law in the form $V = IR$ to substitute for the voltages.

$$I_tR_t = I_1R_1 + I_2R_2$$

Conservation of charge requires that the current through the combination be equal to that through each of the resistors. Therefore, $I_t = I_1 = I_2$ and we can cancel the currents to obtain

---

[3] 1 A through the 12-Ω resistor and 3 A through the 4-Ω resistor

$$R_t = R_1 + R_2$$

resistors in series add

We can perform a similar analysis for the parallel resistors in Fig. 20.3.2. In this case, we know that the total current through the pair must just be the sum of the currents through each one.

$$I_t = I_1 + I_2$$

Substituting for the currents using Ohm's law, we have

$$\frac{V_t}{R_t} = \frac{V_1}{R_1} + \frac{V_2}{R_2}$$

Since the voltage drop across the circuit is independent of the path, we know that $V_t = V_1 = V_2$. Therefore, we can cancel the voltages to obtain our result.

$$\frac{1}{R_t} = \frac{1}{R_1} + \frac{1}{R_2}$$

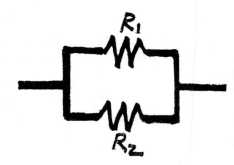

Fig. 20.3.2

resistors in parallel add as reciprocals

20.4 Calculating Electric Power

The power P generated or dissipated in a device can be calculated from knowledge of the current through it and the voltage drop across it.

$$P = IV$$

For a device obeying Ohm's law, we can obtain other equivalent forms for the power. Substituting for the voltage, we get

$$P = IV = I(IR) = I^2R$$

Substituting for the current, we get

$$P = IV = \left(\frac{V}{R}\right)V = \frac{V^2}{R}$$

Example 20.4.1

What is the resistance of a 60-W bulb if it is rated for a voltage of 120 V?

Since we know the power and the voltage, we can use the last equation to find the resistance. Solving for the resistance R and plugging in the given numerical values, we find that

$$R = \frac{V^2}{P} = \frac{(120\,V)^2}{60\,W} = 240\,\Omega$$

Practice[4]

What is the resistance of a 100-W bulb?

Example 20.4.2

The 60-W bulb and the 100-W bulb in Example 20.4.1 are now connected in series and plugged into the 120-V outlet. What is the power dissipated by each one?

When the bulbs are connected in series, their resistances add. Using the values obtained in Example 20.4.1, the total resistance is 384 Ω. This allows us to calculate the current through the circuit.

$$I = \frac{V}{R} = \frac{120\,V}{384\,\Omega} = 0.313\,A$$

Since this is also the current through each bulb, we can calculate the power for each bulb.

$$P_{60} = I^2 R_{60} = (0.313\,A)^2\,(240\,\Omega) = 23.5\,W$$

$$P_{100} = I^2 R_{100} = (0.313\,A)^2\,(144\,\Omega) = 14.1\,W$$

where the subscript refers to the wattage of the bulb. Notice that the power dissipated by each bulb is reduced. This occurs because the voltage across each bulb is less than the 120 V normally used. What is surprising is that the power dissipated in the 100-W bulb is now less than that in the 60-W bulb. For the same currents, more power is dissipated in the bulb with the higher resistance according to $P = I^2 R$.

◆ ◆ ◆

---

[4] 144 Ω

Problems

1. What is the resistance of a gold wire with a diameter of 0.2 mm and a length of 8 cm?

2. What is the resistance of a silver wire with a diameter of 0.01 mm and a length of 50 cm?

3. How long must a copper wire be to have a resistance of 1 Ω if it has a square cross-section 1 mm on a side?

4. What is the diameter of a 100-m long copper wire with a resistance of 5 Ω?

5. What is the total resistance of two 10-Ω resistors connected in series? In parallel?

6. What is the total resistance of a 100-Ω resistor and a 1-Ω resistor connected in parallel? Does your answer agree with the statement that the total resistance is always smaller than the smaller resistance?

7. What is the total resistance of the arrangement of resistors in Fig. 20.P.1?

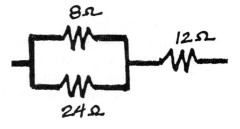

Fig. 20.P.1

8. What is the total resistance of the combination of resistors shown in Fig. 20.P.2?

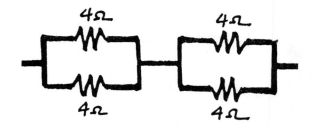

Fig. 20.P.2

*9. What different values of resistance can you get by combining three 6-Ω resistors?

*10. What values of resistance can you make by wiring four 8-Ω resistors together?

11. A light bulb has a resistance of 9 Ω when hot and draws a current of 1/3 A. At what voltage does the bulb operate?

12. What voltage should you use for a bulb with a resistance of 50 Ω if you want it to draw a current of 0.24 A?

13. Two resistors (12 Ω and 24 Ω) are connected in series to a 6-V battery. What is the voltage drop across each resistor?

14. Three resistors are connected in series to a 6-V battery. If the resistances are 4 Ω, 8 Ω, and 12 Ω, what is the voltage drop across each resistor?

15. Two resistors are connected in parallel to a 12-V battery. If the resistances are 8 Ω and 24 Ω, what is the current through each one?

16. If three 360-Ω resistors are connected in parallel to a 6-V battery, what is the total current supplied by the battery?

17. A student holds three 1½-V batteries end to end but one of them is reversed. What voltage would you expect to have from one end of the row to the other?

18. A typical car battery has six 2-V cells. What happens to the output voltage of the battery if one of the cells becomes shorted?

*19. If a string of Christmas tree lights has 10 bulbs, what voltage rating should each bulb have if they are wired in series?

20. What voltage rating should the bulbs in the previous problem have if they are wired in parallel?

*21. The switch shown in Fig. 20.P.3 can be used to connect the wire on the left to either of those on the right. Design a circuit using two of these switches to independently turn a light bulb on and off like the switches at each end of a hallway. Be sure that there are no short circuits when the bulb is off.

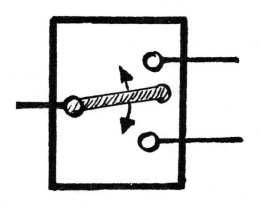

Fig. 20.P.3

*22. The switch shown in Fig. 20.P.4 can be used to reverse the connections between the two wires on the left and the two on the right. Add one of these switches to the circuit in the previous question so that three switches control the same bulb.

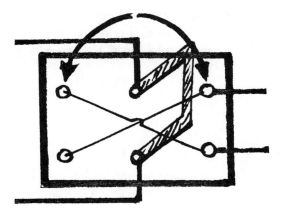

Fig. 20.P.4

23. What power is need to operate a hair dryer with a resistance of 10 Ω?

24. A coffee maker has a resistance of 12 Ω when hot. What power does it require?

25. A toaster is rated at 800 W. If a slice of bread is toasted in 60 s, how much energy is used?

26. How much energy is required to run a 1500-W space heater for a 24-hour day?

27. At a cost of 8¢/kWh, what does it cost to leave a 100-W security light on during a 10-hour night?

28. What does it cost to run a 750-W space heater for 8 hours if electrical energy costs 8¢/kWh?

29. How many 100-W bulbs can be put in parallel on one 120-V circuit before they blow a 15-A fuse?

30. What size fuse is needed if you want to run two 1200-W space heaters on the same circuit?

31. Two 6-Ω resistors are connected in parallel to a 6-V battery. What is the electrical power used? How does this compare to a single 6-Ω resistor connected to the 6-V battery?

*32. Two 6-Ω resistors are connected in series to a 6-V battery. What is the electrical power used? How does this compare to a single 6-Ω resistor connected to the 6-V battery?

*33. If a 10-W and a 20-W bulb are connected in parallel, the 20-W bulb is brighter. Which one is brighter if they are connected in series? Explain.

21 ELECTROMAGNETISM

21.1 Charged Particles in Magnetic Fields

The force exerted on a moving charged particle by a
magnetic field is given by

$$F = qv_\perp B$$

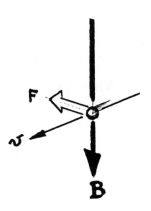

where q is the particle's charge, B is the strength of the
magnetic field, and $v_\perp$ is the component of the velocity
that is perpendicular to the direction of the magnetic
field. The direction of the force is always perpendicular
to the direction of the magnetic field <u>and</u> to the direction
of the velocity as shown in Fig. 21.1.1.

Fig. 21.1.1

For the special case when the velocity v is
perpendicular to the magnetic field, the force has a
constant value and always points at right angles to the
instantaneous velocity. This is a centripetal force that will cause the particle to travel along a
circular path. The centripetal acceleration a of the particle can be written

$$a = \frac{v^2}{r}$$

where r is the radius of the circular path. Since this centripetal acceleration is provided by
the magnetic force, we can also write the acceleration as

$$a = \frac{F}{m} = \frac{qvB}{m}$$

where m is the particle's mass. Equating these two expressions for the acceleration, we have

$$\frac{v^2}{r} = \frac{qvB}{m}$$

Canceling the common factor v and solving for r, we arrive at our expression for the radius
of the circle.

$$r = \frac{mv}{qB}$$

The units of the magnetic field are tesla (T). From our force equation at the top of the
page, we can see that a tesla must have the following equivalent units.

$$T = \frac{N}{C \cdot m/s} = \frac{kg \cdot m}{s^2} \frac{s}{C \cdot m} = \frac{kg}{C \cdot s} = \frac{kg}{A \cdot s^2}$$

Example 21.1.1

What is the acceleration of a proton with a velocity of 3 x 10^6 m/s perpendicular to a magnetic field with a strength of 0.4 T?

$$a = \frac{qvB}{m} = \frac{(1.6 \times 10^{-19} C)(3 \times 10^6 m/s)(0.4 T)}{1.67 \times 10^{-27} kg} = 1.15 \times 10^{14} m/s^2$$

Practice[1]

What is the acceleration if we replace the proton by an electron?

Example 21.1.2

What is the radius of the circular path for the proton in the previous example?

$$r = \frac{mv}{qB} = \frac{(1.67 \times 10^{-27} kg)(3 \times 10^6 m/s)}{(1.6 \times 10^{-19} C)(0.4 T)} = 7.83 \times 10^{-2} m = 7.83 cm$$

Practice[2]

What is the radius for the electron?

Practice

Show that you can get the same radius using the results of Example 21.1.1 and the equation for the centripetal acceleration.

◆ ◆ ◆

21.2 Transformers

The relative size of the voltage produced in the secondary coil of a transformer is given by the ratio of the number of loops in the secondary to the number of loops in the primary. Using the subscripts p and s for primary and secondary, respectively, this gives the following relationship.

---

[1] 2.11 x 10^{17} m/s

[2] 4.27 x 10^{-5} m

$$\frac{V_s}{V_p} = \frac{N_s}{N_p}$$

Example 21.2.1

A transformer is used to reduce the voltage from 120 V to 9 V. If the primary coil has 400 turns, how many coils must the secondary have?

Solving our transformer equation for the number of coils N_s in the secondary, we have

$$N_s = N_p \frac{V_s}{V_p} = (400 \; turns) \frac{9 \, V}{120 \, V} = 30 \; turns$$

Practice[3]

If the transformer had 40 turns in the secondary coil, what would the output voltage be?

◆ ◆ ◆

21.3 Making Waves

Example 21.3.1

According to the text, the range of frequencies for visible light is 4.0-7.5 x 10^{14} Hz. What is the wavelength corresponding to the reddest red light?

Remembering that red light has the lowest frequency, we can calculate the wavelength.

$$\lambda = \frac{c}{f} = \frac{3 \, x \, 10^8 \, m/s}{4.0 \, x \, 10^{14} \, Hz} = 7.5 \, x \, 10^{-7} \, m = 750 \, nm$$

Practice[4]

What is the wavelength of the most violet violet light?

◆ ◆ ◆

---

[3] 12 V

[4] 400 nm

Problems

1. An electron is traveling at 3×10^4 m/s perpendicular to a magnetic field of 4 T. What is the magnetic force on the electron?

2. What is the maximum force a magnetic field of 25 T can exert on a proton traveling at 4×10^6 m/s?

3. An electron traveling at 5×10^5 m/s perpendicular to a magnetic field of 2 T executes a circular path. What is the radius of the circle?

4. What is the radius of the circle followed by a proton with a velocity of 6×10^4 m/s perpendicular to a magnetic field of 3 T?

5. A transformer designed to reduce the voltage from 120 V to 12 V has 1000 turns in the primary. How many turns does it have in the secondary?

6. A transformer designed to reduce the voltage from 24 kV to 120 V has 500 turns in the secondary coil. How many turns does it have in the primary?

7. What output voltage would you expect if the primary has 200 turns, the secondary has 50 turns and the input voltage is 120 V ac?

8. What output voltage would you expect in the previous problem if the input voltage were 120 V dc?

9. Typical microwaves have a wavelength of 1 cm. What is the frequency of these microwaves?

10. What is the frequency of an X ray with a wavelength of 0.1 nm?

11. The eye is most sensitive to yellow-green light with wavelengths around 550 nm. What is the frequency of this light?

12. What is the frequency of the "X-band" radar used by police if it has a wavelength of 2.85 cm?

13. The emergency frequency for airplanes is 121.1 MHz. What is the wavelength of these radio waves?

14. If an FM radio station broadcasts at 97.3 MHz, at what wavelength is it broadcasting?

15. What is the wavelength range of the AM radio band (540 - 1600 kHz)?

16. Channel 2 on your TV set broadcasts in a band from 54 to 60 MHz. What is the corresponding range of wavelengths?

22   THE EARLY ATOM

22.1 Radiating Objects

Example 22.1.1

What frequency is needed to produce quanta with energies of 1 eV?

$$f = \frac{E}{h} = \frac{1 \; eV}{6.63 \; x \; 10^{-34} \; J \cdot s} \left(\frac{1.6 \; x \; 10^{-19} \; J}{1 \; eV} \right) = 2.41 \; x \; 10^{14} \; Hz$$

According to Fig. 21-26 in the text, this frequency is in the infrared range.

Practice[1]

What frequency is needed to produce quanta with twice the energy?

◆ ◆ ◆

22.2 The Photoelectric Effect

The description of the photoelectric effect described in the text can be translated into the equation using the conservation of energy.

$$KE_{max} = hf - \phi$$

where KE_{max} is the maximum kinetic energy of the emitted electrons, hf is the energy of the incident photon, and ϕ is the amount of energy required for an electron to leave the surface. The reason that the equation involves the maximum kinetic energy is that it takes a range of energies for the electrons to get to the surface depending on their locations in the metal. There are many electrons with less than the maximum kinetic energy. The values of the *work function* ϕ for typical metallic surfaces range from 2 eV to 7 eV with most being between 4 eV and 5 eV. Because the kinetic energies of electrons are often expressed in eV, it is useful to write the value of Planck's constant in these units.

$$h = 6.63 \; x \; 10^{-34} \; J \cdot s \left(\frac{1 \; eV}{1.60 \; x \; 10^{-19} \; J} \right) = 4.14 \; x \; 10^{-15} \; eV \cdot s$$

---

[1] Double the frequency

Example 22.2.1

What is the maximum kinetic energy of the photoelectrons emitted when ultraviolet light with a frequency of 2×10^{15} Hz shines on aluminum with $\phi = 4.08$ eV?

$$KE_{max} = hf - \phi = (4.14 \times 10^{-15} \, eV \cdot s)(2 \times 10^{15} \, Hz) - 4.08 \, eV = 4.2 \, eV$$

Practice[2]

What is the maximum kinetic energy for twice the frequency?

Example 22.2.2

What is the minimum frequency that will eject photoelectrons from aluminum?

We set the kinetic energy equal to zero to find out the lowest energy photon that can eject an electron. Notice that this photon must only supply enough energy for the electron to escape the surface. With KE = 0, our equation shows that the photon energy is equal to the work function. Solving for the frequency, we get

$$hf = \phi$$

$$f = \frac{\phi}{h} = \frac{4.08 \, eV}{4.14 \times 10^{-15} \, eV \cdot s} = 9.86 \times 10^{14} \, Hz$$

◆ ◆ ◆

22.3 Bohr's Model

Bohr's restriction on the allowed values of the angular momentum in the hydrogen atom allows the calculation of the values associated with each orbit. We begin by obtaining the values for the ground state, that is, for $n = 1$. The smallest possible angular momentum L_1 is given by

$$L_1 = \frac{h}{2\pi} = \frac{6.63 \times 10^{-34} \, J \cdot s}{6.28} = 1.06 \times 10^{-34} \, J \cdot s$$

The other values are given by $L_n = nL_1$.

---

[2] 12.5 eV

The smallest radius r_1 is given by

$$r_1 = \frac{h^2}{4\pi^2 km e^2} = 5.31 \times 10^{-11} \, m = 0.0531 \, nm$$

where m is the mass of the electron, e is its charge, and k is Coulomb's constant. The other values of the radius are given by $r_n = n^2 r_1$.

The lowest energy is given by

$$E_1 = \frac{-k e^2}{2 r_1} = -2.17 \times 10^{-18} \, J = -13.6 \, eV$$

The energy has a negative value because of the choice made for the zero value of the potential energy. It is chosen to be zero when the electron is located an infinite distance from the nucleus of the atom. This tells us that the electron is bound to the nucleus and requires an energy equal to E_1 to escape. The other values of the energy are given by $E_n = E_1 / n^2$. Notice that even though the energies of the larger orbits are obtained by <u>dividing</u> by n^2, the energies are higher because of the minus sign.

Example 22.3.1

What are the radius and the energy of the first excited state in hydrogen?

$$r_2 = n^2 r_1 = 2^2 (0.0531 \, nm) = 0.212 \, nm$$

$$E_2 = \frac{E_1}{n^2} = \frac{-13.6 \, eV}{2^2} = -3.4 \, eV$$

◆ ◆ ◆

22.4 Atomic Spectra Explained

The energies of the photons emitted when the electrons in hydrogen atoms drop from the mth level to the nth level can be calculated from our expression for the energy of the various levels.

$$E_m - E_n = \frac{E_1}{m^2} - \frac{E_1}{n^2} = E_1 \left(\frac{1}{m^2} - \frac{1}{n^2} \right)$$

Notice that since $m > n$, the term in brackets will be negative and the energy will be positive as expected. It is these photons that comprise the spectral lines given off by hydrogen when the atoms are excited.

Example 22.4.1

What are the energy and the frequency of the photons emitted when electrons in hydrogen drop from the n = 2 level to the n = 1 level?

$$E_2 - E_1 = E_1\left(\frac{1}{2^2} - \frac{1}{1^2}\right) = \frac{-3E_1}{4} = 10.2\,eV$$

We can now calculate the frequency of photons with this energy.

$$f = \frac{E}{h} = \frac{10.2\,eV}{6.63\,x\,10^{-34}\,J\cdot s}\left(\frac{1.60\,x\,10^{-19}\,J}{1\,eV}\right) = 2.46\,x\,10^{15}\,Hz$$

These photons are in the ultraviolet range and are not visible to the naked eye.

Practice[3]

What is the energy of the photons emitted in the n = 3 to n = 2 transition?

◆ ◆ ◆

Problems

1. What is the numerical value of the charge-to-mass ratio of electrons?
2. What is the numerical value of the charge-to-mass ratio for protons?
3. What energy quanta correspond to the frequency ($5.5\,x\,10^{14}$ Hz) where the human eye is most sensitive?
4. What energy quanta correspond to the broadcast frequency (1090 kHz) of KBOZ?
5. What frequency would produce quanta with an energy of 1 J? Does this seem like a realistic frequency?

6. What frequency would produce quanta with an energy of 1 MeV?
7. Light with a frequency of $1.5\,x\,10^{15}$ Hz shines on a copper surface ($\phi = 4.70$ eV). What is the maximum kinetic energy of the photoelectrons?
8. What is the maximum kinetic energy of the photoelectrons emitted when light with a frequency of $4\,x\,10^{15}$ Hz shines on a zinc surface that has a work function of 4.31 eV?

---

[3] 1.89 eV

9. What is the minimum frequency that will produce photoelectrons from a silver surface with a work function of 4.73 eV?

10. A polished surface of platinum ($\phi =$ 6.35 eV) is illuminated by light with a frequency of 1.2×10^{15} eV. Will photoelectrons be emitted?

11. What is the angular momentum of the electron in the second Bohr orbit?

12. Show that the units of Planck's constant are those of angular momentum.

13. What is the radius of the second excited state in hydrogen?

14. What is the radius of the $n = 4$ state in hydrogen?

15. What is the energy of the second excited state in hydrogen?

16. What is the energy of the $n = 4$ state in hydrogen?

17. How much energy is required to remove the electron from the hydrogen atom when it is in the first excited state?

18. What is the energy of the photon that is released when the electron drops from the $n = 3$ to the $n = 1$ level?

19. Is the photon given off in the previous problem in the visible, ultraviolet, or X-ray range of the electromagnetic spectrum?

20. What color is emitted when the electrons in hydrogen atoms drop from the $n = 4$ to the $n = 2$ level?

21. What is the frequency emitted when an electron is captured into the ground state of hydrogen?

22. What frequency is emitted when electrons in hydrogen drops from the $n = 3$ level to the $n = 1$ level?

23   THE MODERN ATOM

23.1 De Broglie's Waves

Louis de Broglie showed that particles have wave properties as well as particle properties. The wavelength associated with these particles is given by

$$\lambda = \frac{h}{mv}$$

where h is Planck's constant, m is the mass of the particle, and v is the speed of the particle.

Example 23.1.1

What is the wavelength of an electron with a kinetic energy of 1 eV?

Because the de Broglie relationship depends on momentum, we need to find the momentum of the electron first. Starting with the definition of kinetic energy and treating the electron nonrelativistically, we have

$$KE = \frac{1}{2}mv^2$$

If we multiply both sides of the equation by $2m$, we get

$$m^2v^2 = 2mKE = 2(9.11 \times 10^{-31} kg)(1\,eV)\left(\frac{1.6 \times 10^{-19} J}{1\,eV}\right)$$

$$= 2.92 \times 10^{-49} \frac{kg^2 \cdot m^2}{s^2}$$

and

$$mv = 5.4 \times 10^{-25} kg \cdot m/s$$

Putting this value in the de Broglie relationship, we have

$$\lambda = \frac{h}{mv} = \frac{6.63 \times 10^{-34} J \cdot s}{5.4 \times 10^{-25} kg \cdot m/s} = 1.23 \times 10^{-9} m = 1.23\,nm$$

This wavelength is about 10 times the spacing between atoms in a crystal.

Practice[1]

What happens to the wavelength if the electron has 10 times the kinetic energy?

◆ ◆ ◆

23.2 The Uncertainty Principle

The Heisenberg uncertainty principle puts limits on the simultaneous measurements of a particle's position and momentum. This relationship can be used to make estimates of a number of effects that will give us some insight into subatomic phenomena.

Example 23.2.1

A beam of electrons with a speed of $v = 10^4$ m/s passes through a vertical slit with a width $w = 20$ μm. What is the width of the diffraction pattern produced on a screen located $L = 1$ m away?

Let's first estimate the answer using the uncertainty principle. We can do this because confining the electrons to pass through the slit gives an uncertainty in their positions in the horizontal direction and, thus, creates an uncertainty in their horizontal component of momentum. This means that even though the electrons were aimed face on to the slit, they can emerge from the other side with a sideways component of the momentum. This sideways component means that the electron can hit the screen to either side of the center line.

$$\Delta p \, \Delta y > h$$

The uncertainty in the horizontal position Δx is equal to w. To do calculations, we set the two sides of the relationship "approximately equal" to each other. Solving for Δp, we can find the uncertainty in the component of the momentum in the horizontal direction.

$$\Delta p \approx \frac{h}{\Delta y} = \frac{h}{w}$$

Let's calculate the location of the edge of this central maximum by assuming that the sideways component of the momentum p is equal to Δp. If we use the symbol y for the sideways displacement of the electrons with this momentum, we can calculate its position as follows

---

[1] The wavelength decreases by the square root of 10 or a factor of 3.16. Therefore, $\lambda = 0.39$ nm

$$y = vt = \frac{pt}{m}$$

Substituting in our value for p and realizing that $t = L/v$, we have

$$y = \frac{pt}{m} = \frac{1}{m}\frac{h}{w}\frac{L}{v} = \frac{hL}{wmv}$$

Plugging in the numerical values, we get our estimate.

$$y = \frac{hL}{wmv} = \frac{(6.63 \times 10^{-34}\,J{\cdot}s)(1\,m)}{(20 \times 10^{-6}\,m)(9.11 \times 10^{-31}\,kg)(10^4\,m/s)} = 3.64\,mm$$

Therefore, the width of the central maximum of the electron diffraction pattern is roughly 7 mm.

We can check to see if this makes sense by looking at the wave aspects of the electrons using the techniques of Section 14.10 with $m = 1$. This yields

$$y_{min} = \frac{\lambda L}{w}$$

Using the de Broglie relationship from the last section, we can insert the wavelength of the electrons.

$$y_{min} = \frac{\lambda L}{w} = \frac{h}{mv}\frac{L}{w} = \frac{hL}{wmv}$$

Since this agrees with our previous result, we find that the two methods give the same result although they approached the problem from very different directions.

◆ ◆ ◆

Example 23.2.2

If the half-life of an excited state in an atom is 10^{-8} s, what is the uncertainty in the energy of the photon emitted when electrons in this state jump to the ground state?

This time we use the uncertainty principle between energy and time.

$$\Delta E\,\Delta t > h$$

Let's set the two sides of the relationship "approximately equal" to each other and assume that the uncertainty in the time it takes the excited state to decay is equal to the half-life. Then solving for ΔE, we get the following for the uncertainty in the energy of the excited state.

$$\Delta E \approx \frac{h}{\Delta t} = \frac{6.63 \times 10^{-34} \, J \cdot s}{10^{-8} \, s} = 6.63 \times 10^{-26} \, J \approx 4 \times 10^{-7} \, eV$$

Since the ground state is stable, we can safely assume that the uncertainty in its energy is even smaller. This uncertainty in the energy level is less than one millionth of an electron volt. Although the uncertainty in the energy of the emitted photons is very small compared to their average energy, the uncertainty can be observed as a broadening of the spectral line.

◆ ◆ ◆

Problems

1. What is the wavelength of an electron traveling at 1% of the speed of light?

2. A proton has a speed of 3×10^6 m/s. What is its wavelength?

3. What is the wavelength of a baseball (mass = 0.14 kg) thrown at 45 m/s?

4. How big is the wavelength of a car (mass = 1500 kg) traveling at 30 m/s compared to the size of an atom (0.1 nm)?

5. What is the wavelength of a proton with a kinetic energy of 1 eV? Why is this different than the value calculated for the 1-eV electron in Example 23.1.1?

6. If a proton has a kinetic energy of 10 eV, what is its wavelength. How does this value compare to that of the 10-eV electron in the Practice problem of Example 23.1.1?

*7. What is the kinetic energy of an electron with a wavelength equal to the diameter of a hydrogen atom (0.1 nm)?

*8. What is the kinetic energy of a proton that has a wavelength equal to the diameter of a hydrogen atom (0.1 nm)?

*9. In order for an electron to be confined in a nucleus, its wavelength must be smaller than the size of the nucleus (say 10^{-14} m). What is the kinetic energy of such an electron calculated non-relativistically? What does this say about the possibility of an electron existing in a nucleus?

*10. Obviously a neutron can exist in a nucleus. Using the idea in the previous problem, show that a neutron would have a kinetic energy much smaller than its rest mass energy.

11. If a light is used to locate an electron to a precision of 2 nm, what is the uncertainty in the velocity of the electron?

12. If a beam of electrons pass through a vertical slit with a width of 50 μm, what is the uncertainty in the horizontal component of their velocity?

13. If the velocity of an electron is determined with a precision of 20 m/s, what is the uncertainty in its position?

14. If the velocity of a proton is determined with a precision of 20 m/s, what is the uncertainty in its position?

15. A beam of electrons with a speed of 10^5 m/s passes through a vertical slit (width = 50 μm) forming a diffraction pattern on a screen 75 cm away. Use the uncertainty principle to calculate the width of the central maximum?

16. What happens to the width of the diffraction pattern in the previous problem if a proton beam is used?

17. If an excited state has a half-life of 10^{-16} s, what is the uncertainty in the energy of the state?

18. If the uncertainty in the energy of an excited state is a billionth of an electron volt, what is the half-life of the state?

24 THE NUCLEUS

24.1 Radioactive Decay

Half the number of nuclei in a radioactive sample decay in a characteristic time known as the half-life $T_{1/2}$. After a second half-life has elapsed, one-half of the remaining nuclei will have decayed. After a third half-life, one-half of those still remaining decay. And so on. This means that one-half of the original sample remains after $T_{1/2}$, one-half of one-half (or one-fourth) remain after $2T_{1/2}$, and one-half of one-fourth (or one-eighth) of the original sample remains after $3T_{1/2}$. And the process theoretically continues forever. This can be written mathematically in the following way.

$$N = N_o \left(\frac{1}{2} \right)^n$$

where N is the number of nuclei remaining, N_0 is the number of nuclei present at the beginning of the time period, and n is the number of half-lives that have elapsed.

The activity of a radioactive sample depends on the number of nuclei that decay in a unit of time. Usually this is the number of decays per second. As an example, the activity of 1 g of radium is 3.7×10^{10} decays/s, a unit named the curie (Ci), after Marie Curie. Since the number of decays is equal to the change in the number of nuclei remaining, we can write the activity as $\Delta N / \Delta t$. Changing the N to ΔN in the equation above and dividing both sides of the previous equation by Δt, we get a relationship that shows how the activity of a sample decreases with time.

$$\frac{\Delta N}{\Delta t} = \left(\frac{\Delta N}{\Delta t} \right)_o \left(\frac{1}{2} \right)^n$$

where the term in parentheses with the subscript o denotes the activity at the start of the time period. Because the activity is proportional to the number of nuclei present at that time, the number of nuclei and the activity change at the same rate.

Example 24.1.1

> The half-life of radium is 1620 years. A 1-g sample of radium contains 2.66×10^{21} nuclei. How many of these will remain after 8000 years?

> We first need to know the number of half-lives that have elapsed. This is obtained by dividing the time period T by the half-life $T_{1/2}$.

$$n = \frac{T}{T_{1/2}} = \frac{8000 \ y}{1620 \ y} \approx 5$$

where we have rounded off the value of n to the nearest integer to avoid complications. We can now calculate how many nuclei will remain after 5 half-lives.

$$N = N_o \left(\frac{1}{2}\right)^n = N_o \left(\frac{1}{2^5}\right) = \frac{2.66 \ x \ 10^{21}}{32} = 8.31 \ x \ 10^{19}$$

Practice[1]

How many radium nuclei will remain after an additional 8000 years?

Example 24.1.2

What is the activity of the 1-g of radium after 8000 years?

Since the original activity is 1 Ci by definition, the activity after 8000 years will be

$$\frac{\Delta N}{\Delta t} = \left(\frac{\Delta N}{\Delta t}\right)_o \left(\frac{1}{2}\right)^n = \frac{1 \ Ci}{32} = 0.0313 \ Ci = 1.16 \ x \ 10^9 \ decays/s$$

◆ ◆ ◆

24.2 Radioactive Clocks

Because the decay of a radioactive sample is so regular and predictable, the decay can be used as a clock. We need only monitor the activity of a sample to know how much time has elapsed. If we can determine how many half-lives n have elapsed, we can calculate the time T from a knowledge of the half-life $T_{1/2}$.

$$T = nT_{1/2}$$

One of the most common radioactive decays used in the dating of organic substances is that of carbon-14. The ratio of C-14 to the stable C-12 has a constant value of $1.3 \ x \ 10^{-12}$ in the atmosphere. (High energy particles from space create C-14 via collisions with nuclei to replace the ones that decay.) Although this means that only about one in a trillion carbon atoms is radioactive, this is enough to be easily detected. As an example, a 1-g sample of carbon has about $5 \ x \ 10^{22}$ atoms, of which some 65 billion are radioactive. The activity of

---

[1] $2.6 \ x \ 10^{18}$

this sample would be about 16 decays/min.

The key to radiocarbon dating is understanding that living organism exchange air with the atmosphere. Therefore, the ratio of the two carbon isotopes in the organism is the same as the known value in the atmosphere. However, when the organism dies, the exchange stops and because the C-14 decays into another element, the ratio decreases. Therefore, if we can determine that activity per gram of carbon, we can determine how many half-lives have elapsed. Knowing that the half-life of C-14 is 5730 y, we can then determine how long ago the organism died.

Example 24.2.1

A sample of carbon from a piece of charred wood from a campfire has an activity of 4 decays/min/g. How long ago was the campsite occupied?

Because the activity was 16 decays/min/g when the wood was chopped down for the fire, the activity has been reduced by a factor of 4. Therefore, two half-lives have elapsed, or

$$T = nT_{1/2} = 2(5730\,y) = 11{,}460\,y$$

Practice[2]

How old is the campsite if the activity is only 2 decays/min/g?

◆ ◆ ◆

24.3 Radiation and Matter

The passage of gamma rays through matter is analogous to radioactive decay. The number of gamma rays surviving after a characteristic "half-distance" is one-half of those at the beginning. During the next half-distance, only one-half of the half survive. And so on. Therefore, repeating the logic of Section 24.1, we can write down the number N surviving after n half-distances as

$$N = N_o \left(\frac{1}{2}\right)^n$$

where N_o is the initial number.

―――――――――――――

[2] 17,200 y

Example 24.3.1

If a burst of 1000 gamma rays with an energy of 5 MeV is incident on a 18.2-cm thick aluminum plate, how many gamma rays exit the other side of the plate?

From Table 24-4 in the text, we find that the half-distance for 5-MeV gamma rays in aluminum is 9.1 cm. Therefore, the plate is two half-distances thick and the number of gamma rays coming out the other side is

$$N = N_o \left(\frac{1}{2}\right)^n = 1000 \left(\frac{1}{2^2}\right) = 250$$

◆ ◆ ◆

Problems

1. What is the activity of 1 kg of radium?
2. How much radium would you need to have an activity of 10^{12} decays/s?
3. If you initially have 10^{20} radioactive nuclei, how many will remain after 10 half-lives?
4. How many nuclei from an initial sample of 4×10^{24} radioactive nuclei will remain after 7 half-lives?
5. If you start with 1 μg of a radioactive sample, how much will you have left after 4 half-lives?
6. Zirconium-87 undergoes beta plus decay with a half-life of 1.6 h. How much of a 2-mg sample will remain after 8 h?
7. The half-life for argon-37 to decay via electron capture is 34.3 days. If its initial activity is 32 μCi, what is its activity after 137 days?

8. Potassium-40 is a naturally occurring radioactive nucleus that is present in our bodies and is the major internal contributor to the background radiation we experience. With a half-life of 1.3×10^9 y, what change in the activity of potassium-40 has occurred since the earth was formed some 4.5 billion years ago?
9. Tritium (the heavy, heavy isotope of hydrogen) decays via beta minus decay with a half-life of 12.3 y. How long must one wait for more than 99% of a sample of tritium to decay?
10. One of the radioactive nuclei produced in nuclear reactors is uranium-239 which undergoes beta minus decay with a half-life of 23.5 min. How long after the reactor is shut down will the number of uranium-239 nuclei be reduced by a factor of 1000?

11. If a gram of carbon from an axe handle has an activity of 1 decay/min, how old is the axe handle?

12. The activity of a gram of carbon from a piece of an ancient boat is 30 decays/h. What is the age of the boat?

13. If 5 g of carbon from the leg bone of a mummified goat has an activity of 20 decays/min, what is the age of the mummy?

*14. If the activity of a gram of carbon is 11.3 decays/min, how old is the sample?

15. The half-life of uranium-238 is 4.5 billion years. If its activity has decreased by a factor of 2 since the formation of the earth, how old is the earth?

16. Tritium has a half-life of 12.3 y and can also be used to date organic matter. If the activity of tritium is determined to be 3% of the expected activity, what is the age of the sample?

17. What fraction of the 1-MeV gamma rays incident on a 12.6-cm aluminum block will emerge from the other side?

18. The half-distance of 15-MeV gamma rays in lead is 1.0 cm. If 1 billion 15-MeV gamma rays enter a lead block with a thickness of 10 cm, how many will emerge from the other side?

19. A beam with an intensity of 10^6 gamma rays per second hits an aluminum shield with a thickness of 1 m. If the gamma rays have an energy of 10 MeV, what is the intensity of the beam exiting the shield?

20. What thickness of aluminum is required to reduce the intensity of a 5-MeV beam of gamma rays to less than 0.1% of the original intensity?

25 NUCLEAR ENERGY

In this chapter we will be discussing very small effects. The experiments, however, are very precise, so we can justify using more than our usual three significant digits.

25.1 Nuclear Binding Energy

It is useful to have the energy equivalent of 1 amu when doing calculations with nuclear binding energies. Using Einstein's formula $E = mc^2$, we have

$$1.6605 \times 10^{-27} \, kg \, (2.9979 \times 10^8 \, m/s)^2 \left(\frac{1 \, MeV}{1.6022 \times 10^{-13} \, J} \right) = 931.44 \, MeV$$

Example 25.1.1

What is the average binding energy of $^{56}_{26}$Fe?

We begin by calculating the mass of the 26 protons and 30 neutrons that make up the iron nucleus. Then we look up the mass of the iron nucleus and calculate the mass difference.

$$
\begin{array}{lllll}
26 \, m_p & = 26 \times 1.00728 & amu = & 26.18928 & amu \\
30 \, m_n & = 30 \times 1.00867 & amu = & + \, \underline{30.26010} & amu \\
 & & & 56.44938 & amu \\
 & m_{Fe} & = & - \, \underline{55.9184} & amu \\
 & & & 0.5310 & amu
\end{array}
$$

We now convert this mass to its energy equivalent using the conversion factor that we developed earlier.

$$0.531 \, amu \left(\frac{931.44 \, MeV}{1 \, amu} \right) = 494.6 \, MeV$$

Dividing this energy by 56, the number of nucleons, we get the average binding energy to be 8.83 MeV/nucleon.

Practice[1]

What is the average binding energy of the deuteron if it has a mass of 2.01355 amu?

Example 25.1.2

Estimate the mass of $^{240}_{94}$Pu given that the binding energy for nuclei this size is 7.5 MeV/nucleon.

The total binding energy of the nucleus is

$$(240 \; nucleons) \left(7.5 \; \frac{MeV}{nucleon} \right) = 1800 \; MeV$$

which can be converted to its mass equivalent.

$$1800 \; MeV \left(\frac{1 \; amu}{931.44 \; MeV} \right) = 1.93 \; amu$$

We now add up the masses to get the total mass of the plutonium-240.

94 m_p =	94	x 1.00728	amu =		94.68432	amu
146 m_n =	146	x 1.00867	amu =	+	147.26582	amu
					241.95014	amu
		binding energy	=	-	1.93	amu
					240.02	amu

This compares well with the actual mass of 240.00 amu.

◆ ◆ ◆

25.2 Nuclear Fission

We can use the graph of the average binding energy (Fig. 25-28 in the text) to obtain an estimate of the energy released in the fission process. Since the fission reaction must conserve the number of nucleons, any change in energy must come from differences in the binding energy.

---

[1] 1.12 MeV/nucleon

Example 25.2.1

One of the fission reactions that takes place is

$$\frac{1}{0}n + \frac{235}{92}U \rightarrow \frac{141}{56}Ba + \frac{92}{36}Kr + 3\ (\frac{1}{0}n)$$

If the average binding energies for the uranium, barium, and krypton are 7.6, 8.4, and 8.5 MeV/nucleon, respectively, how much energy is released in the fission process?

The initial binding energy is

$$235\ nucleons\ \left(7.6\ \frac{MeV}{nucleon}\right) = 1786\ MeV$$

The binding energy of the fission products is

$$141\ nucleons\ \left(8.4\ \frac{MeV}{nucleon}\right) + 92\ nucleons\ \left(8.5\ \frac{MeV}{nucleon}\right) = 1966\ MeV$$

Therefore, 180 MeV are released in the fission reaction. The average energy released in all of the fission reactions for uranium-235 is 208 MeV.

◆ ◆ ◆

25.3 Nuclear Reactors

In a nuclear reactor using uranium as a fuel, the average amount of energy released in each fission reaction is 208 MeV. Knowing this allows us to calculate how many reactions must take place each second to release a given amount of energy. We begin by converting the energy in MeV to the equivalent value in joules.

$$208\ MeV\ \left(\frac{1.6\ x\ 10^{-13}\ J}{1\ MeV}\right) = 3.33\ x\ 10^{-11}\ J$$

This means that every watt requires

$$1\ W = 1\ \frac{J}{s}\ \left(\frac{1\ reaction}{3.33\ x\ 10^{-11}\ J}\right) = 3\ x\ 10^{10}\ reactions/s$$

Example 25.3.1

How many fission reactions per second are required to release 20 MW of thermal energy?

$$20 \times 10^6 \, W \left(\frac{3 \times 10^{10} \, reactions/s}{1 \, W} \right) = 6 \times 10^{17} \, reactions/s$$

Practice[2]

What is the rate of fission reactions required for a 200-MW reactor?

Example 25.3.2

Uranium ore contains 0.7% U-235, most of the rest being U-238. Imagine that we could somehow collect a kilogram of pure U-235 and that all of it were to fission, how much energy would be released?

Since we know that 235 g of U-235 contains Avogadro's number of atoms, we have a total of

$$6.02 \times 10^{23} \, nuclei \left(\frac{1000 \, g}{235 \, g} \right) = 2.56 \times 10^{24} \, nuclei$$

The energy released by these nuclei is

$$2.56 \times 10^{24} \, nuclei \left(\frac{3.33 \times 10^{-11} \, J}{1 \, nucleus} \right) = 8.52 \times 10^{13} \, J$$

To get a better feeling for how much energy this is, let's convert the energy to kilowatt-hours. A kilowatt-hour is the energy provided by a kilowatt power source during each hour of operation.

$$8.52 \times 10^{13} \, J \left(\frac{1 \, kWh}{3.6 \times 10^6 \, J} \right) = 2.37 \times 10^7 \, kWh$$

Let's assume an efficiency of 35% for converting this thermal energy to electrical energy and that a typical household uses 12,000 kWh/y. Then we can calculate the number of households that this kilogram could supply.

$$(2.37 \times 10^7 \, kWh)(0.35) \left(\frac{1 \, household}{12,000 \, kWh} \right) = 694 \, households$$

◆ ◆ ◆

----

[2] 1.2×10^{18} reactions/s

25.4 Fusion Reactors

Example 25.4.1

How much energy is released in the following reaction in which two isotopes of hydrogen - deuterium and tritium - fuse to form helium and a neutron?

$$^{2}_{1}H + ^{3}_{1}H \rightarrow ^{4}_{2}He + ^{1}_{0}n$$

We can get our answer by taking the difference in the total mass before the reaction and the total mass after the reaction.

$$
\begin{aligned}
m_d &= 2.01355 \text{ amu} \\
m_t &= +\ 3.01550 \text{ amu} \\
m_{He} &= -\ 4.00150 \text{ amu} \\
m_n &= -\ \underline{1.00867} \text{ amu} \\
&0.01888 \text{ amu}
\end{aligned}
$$

Converting this mass to energy, we find that 17.6 MeV of energy is released. This is about 3.5 MeV/nucleon. Therefore, this process is more efficient than the fissioning of uranium.

◆ ◆ ◆

25.5 Solar Power

The source of the sun's energy is the fusion of hydrogen to form helium. Although the process takes place in many steps, the net effect can be summarized as follows.

$$4\ ^{1}_{1}H \rightarrow ^{4}_{2}He + 2\ \beta^{+} + 2\ \nu + \text{energy}$$

Including the energy of the neutrinos ν and the photons due to the annihilation of the two positrons, the total energy released is 26.7 MeV.

Example 25.5.1

How much energy would be released by the complete fusion of 1 kg of hydrogen to form helium?

We know that 1 gram of hydrogen contains Avogadro's number of hydrogen nuclei, so 1 kg will contain 1000 times as many, or 6.02×10^{26} nuclei. Since each four hydrogen nuclei will release 26.7 MeV, the total energy released is

$$6.02 \times 10^{26} \, nuclei \left(\frac{26.7 \, MeV}{4 \, nuclei} \right) = 4.02 \times 10^{27} \, MeV = 6.43 \times 10^{14} \, J$$

Therefore, we see that 1 kg of hydrogen releases about 7.5 times as much energy as 1 kg of uranium (see Example 25.3.2).

♦   ♦   ♦

Problems

1. What is the momentum (in MeV/c where c is the speed of light) of a proton with a wavelength of 1 fm?

2. What is the momentum (in MeV/c where c is the speed of light) of an electron with a wavelength of 0.1 fm?

3. Given that the mass of the helium nucleus is 0.0304 amu less that its constituents, verify that the binding energy for the helium nucleus is equal to 28.3 MeV.

4. If the mass of the $^{206}_{82}$Pb nucleus has a mass 1.7425 amu less that the total mass of its neutrons and protons, what is its average binding energy in MeV/nucleon?

5. Calculate the average binding energy per nucleon of the C-12 nucleus given that its mass is 11.9967 amu. (The mass of the neutral atom is 12.0000 amu. The mass of the 6 electrons has been subtracted from this and the binding energy of the electrons to the nucleus has been neglected.)

6. Given that the mass of the U-235 nucleus is 234.9934 amu, calculate the average binding energy per nucleon of the U-235 nucleus.

7. The average binding energy is 8 MeV/nucleon when the total number of nucleons is around 170. What is the estimated mass of $^{170}_{70}$Yb?

8. What is the estimated mass of $^{100}_{44}$Ru if the average binding energy for this region is 8.5 MeV/nucleon?

9. Use the atomic masses given below to calculate the energy released when U-236 fissions to produce Cs-141 and Rb-93.

n	1.00867
U-236	236.04556
Cs-141	140.91963
Rb-93	92.92157

10. If a uranium nucleus were to split evenly into two nuclei with the same number of nucleons (a rare occurrence) while releasing 2 neutrons, how much energy would be released?

11. How many fission reactions must take place each second in a nuclear reactor with a thermal rating of 3 GW?

12. A fission reactor is being designed with a thermal power rating of 500 MW. How many fission reactions must take place each second?

13. How many grams of U-235 would be needed each hour in a power plant with a thermal rating of 400 MW?

14. The total world uses energy at a rate of 7×10^{12} W. How many grams of U-235 would be required each hour to produce this power?

*15. A desalination plant produces a 100 cubic meters of water an hour. How many grams of U-235 would be needed each hour if the process is 100% efficient and the heat is not recycled?

16. The total world uses energy at a rate of 7×10^{12} W. How many kilograms of hydrogen would be required each second to produce this power?

17. Given that the mass of ^3_2He is 3.01493 amu and using the masses given in Example 25.4.1, how much energy is released in the following fusion reaction?

$$^3_2\text{He} + {}^3_2\text{He} \rightarrow {}^4_2\text{He} + {}^1_1\text{H} + {}^1_1\text{H}$$

18. Given that the mass of ^3_2He is 3.01493 amu and using the masses in Example 25.4.1, how much energy is released in the following fusion reaction?

$$^2_1\text{H} + {}^2_1\text{H} \rightarrow {}^3_2\text{He} + {}^1_0\text{n}$$

19. Given that the present energy radiated by the sun each second is about 3.83 $\times 10^{26}$ W, what is the decrease in the mass of the sun in 1 s?

*20. Given that the power output of the sun is 3.83×10^{26} W, how many hydrogen nuclei must be converted to helium each second?

26 ELEMENTARY PARTICLES

26.1 Antimatter

When a positron - the antiparticle of the electron - is slowed down in matter, it is usually captured by an electron to form an "atom" called *positronium*. The electron and positron orbit each other about their common center of mass. Within a microsecond, the two annihilate each other to produce two or more photons. If the positronium was at rest, the total momentum before the annihilation was zero. Therefore, it must be zero afterwards. If there are only two photons produced, they must leave with equal and opposite momenta. These means that each photon carries off one-half of the total energy. Since the positron and the electron have the same mass, each photon must have an energy equal to the rest-mass energy of the electron. (We are ignoring the orbital kinetic energy and the electric potential energy, which are very small compared to the rest-mass energy.)

Example 26.1.1

What is the energy of one of the photons emitted in the annihilation of a positron and an electron?

$$E_\gamma = m_e c^2 = (9.11 \times 10^{-31} \, kg)(3 \times 10^8 \, m/s)^2 = 8.2 \times 10^{-14} \, J$$

Since a joule is a very large energy unit on the atomic and subatomic scales, it is common practice to convert this to electron volts.

$$E_\gamma = 8.2 \times 10^{-14} \, J \left(\frac{1 \, eV}{1.6 \times 10^{-19} \, J} \right) = 5.13 \times 10^5 \, eV = 0.513 \, MeV$$

Therefore, each photon has about one-half a million electron volts of energy.

Let's calculate the frequency of these photons to determine their place in the electromagnetic spectrum.

$$f = \frac{E}{h} = \frac{8.2 \times 10^{-14} \, J}{6.63 \times 10^{-34} \, J \cdot s} = 1.24 \times 10^{20} \, Hz$$

This frequency is in the ranges of X rays and gamma rays. They are usually called gamma rays.

Practice[1]

> What is the energy (in MeV) of the photons emitted in the two-photon annihilation of a proton and an antiproton?

◆ ◆ ◆

26.2 Exchange Particles

We can use the Heisenberg uncertainty principle to obtain an estimate of the range of the strong nuclear force. As discussed in the text, physicists believe that all forces are due to the exchange of particles. For instance, the electromagnetic force is due to the exchange of photons. The force between two nucleons can be considered to be due to the exchange of particles such as the pion.

Let's consider the interaction between a neutron and a proton at rest. Suppose that the neutron spontaneously emits a pion that is absorbed by the proton. According to classical physics, there is a problem. A neutron at rest has a total energy equal to its rest-mass energy $m_n c^2$, where m_n is the mass of the neutron. Even if the pion is emitted with no momentum, the total energy of the neutron and pion after the emission is $m_n c^2 + m_\pi c^2$, where m_π is the mass of the pion. This is a violation of the conservation of energy by $m_\pi c^2$. In general, the violation will be larger than this because the pion and neutron will each have some kinetic energy.

Although such violations of energy are forbidden in classical physics, they are allowed in quantum physics as long as the violations do not last too long. In practice, the violation is corrected when the proton absorbs the pion on the other end of the process. But how long is too long? The violation lasts too long if the uncertainty principle doesn't prevent us from measuring it. In the limiting case, the uncertainty principle involving energy and time states

$$\Delta E \, \Delta t \approx h$$

where the symbol $\approx$ means "approximately equal to." Therefore, the maximum time Δt that a violation can last depends on the value of ΔE.

We can get an upper estimate of the distance the exchange particle can travel by knowing that it cannot exceed the speed of light. Therefore, the exchange particle cannot travel any farther than

$$d_{\max} < c \, \Delta t \approx \frac{c h}{\Delta E}$$

where the symbol $<$ means "less than."

Since photons have zero rest-mass and travel at the speed of light, we can use this

---

[1] 938 MeV

relationship to see why the electrostatic force has an infinite range and why it gets weaker with increasing distance. If the energy of the exchanged photon is small, its effect on the particles is small. This makes sense since the photon has a small momentum. According to our relationship, a small ΔE means a large range. Therefore, the force is weak at long range. On the other hand, a photon with a larger energy will cause a stronger interaction. However, it has a larger ΔE and, consequently, a shorter range.

Example 26.2.1

What is the maximum range of a 1-eV photon emitted by a proton at rest?

$$d_{max} < \frac{c\,h}{\Delta E} = \frac{(3 \times 10^8 \, m/s)(6.63 \times 10^{-34} \, J \cdot s)}{(1 \, eV)} \left(\frac{1 \, eV}{1.6 \times 10^{-19} \, J} \right) \approx 10^{-6} \, m$$

Example 26.2.2

What is the maximum range of the strong nuclear force if it is due to the exchange of pions?

Let's begin by calculating the maximum time the violation can last for the minimum violation of creating the pion at rest. Any other violation would have to last for less time.

$$\Delta t \approx \frac{h}{\Delta E} = \frac{6.63 \times 10^{-34} \, J \cdot s}{(140 \, MeV)} \left(\frac{1 \, MeV}{1.6 \times 10^{-13} \, J} \right) \approx 3 \times 10^{-23} \, s$$

where 140 MeV is the rest-mass energy of the pion. Although this pion was assumed to be at rest, we can still get a maximum range by assuming that it cannot travel faster than light. In a more realistic calculation, the time would be a factor of 10 or more smaller than our number. This is not terribly important as we are only trying to get an idea of the maximum range.

$$d_{max} < c \, \Delta t = (3 \times 10^8 \, m/s)(3 \times 10^{-23} \, s) \approx 9 \times 10^{-15} \, m = 9 \, fm$$

Notice that this result is in rough agreement with the range of 3 fermis stated in the text. Besides, we were calculating a number that we knew was too big.

Practice[2]

If part of the interaction is due to the exchange of kaons (mass = 494 MeV), what is the maximum range of this part of the interaction?

---

[2] 3 fm

Problems

1. If a neutron and an antineutron annihilate at rest to form two photons, what is the energy (in MeV) of each photon?

2. The negative pion is the antiparticle of the positive pion (and vice versa). If these two pions annihilate to form two photons, what is the energy of each? The mass of each pion is 2.48×10^{-28} kg.

3. What is the frequency of the photon in problem 1?

4. What is the frequency of the photon in problem 2?

5. What is the maximum range of a 1-MeV photon emitted by a particle at rest?

6. If a particle at rest emits a 1-keV photon, what maximum range will it have?

7. What energy exchange photon would have the same maximum range as that for the pion in Example 26.2.2?

8. The maximum range of the kaon can be calculated to be about 3 fm. What energy exchange photon has the same maximum range?

9. What is the maximum range of the interaction due to the exchange of etas with a rest-mass energy 549 MeV?

10. The rest-mass energy of the W intermediate vector boson is 80.6 GeV. What is the range of this part of the weak nuclear force?

11. If the rest-mass energy of the Z intermediate vector boson is 91.2 GeV, what is the range of this part of the weak nuclear force?

APPENDIX

Physical Constants and Data

Acceleration due to Gravity	$g = 9.81$ m/s^2
Atomic Mass Unit	$amu = 1.66 \times 10^{-27}$ kg
Avogadro's Number	$N_A = 6.02 \times 10^{23}$ particles/g-mol
Bohr Radius	$r_o = 5.29 \times 10^{-11}$ m
Density of Water	$D_w = 1.00 \times 10^3$ kg/m^3
Electron Volt	$eV = 1.60 \times 10^{-19}$ J
Elementary Charge	$e = 1.60 \times 10^{-19}$ C
Coulomb's Constant	$k = 8.99 \times 10^9$ N·m^2/C^2
Gravitational Constant	$G = 6.67 \times 10^{-11}$ N·m^2/kg^2
Mass of Electron	$m_e = 9.11 \times 10^{-31}$ kg
Mass of Proton	$m_p = 1.673 \times 10^{-27}$ kg
Mass of Neutron	$m_n = 1.675 \times 10^{-27}$ kg
Planck's Constant	$h = 6.63 \times 10^{-34}$ J·s
Speed of Light	$c = 3.00 \times 10^8$ m/s
Speed of Sound (20°C, 1 atm)	$v_s = 343$ m/s
Standard Atmospheric Pressure	$P_{atm} = 1.01 \times 10^5$ Pa

Geometry

Pi	$\pi = 3.14159$
Circumference of Circle	$C = 2\pi r$
Area of Circle	$A = \pi r^2$
Volume of Cylinder	$V = \pi r^2 \ell$
Surface Area of Sphere	$A = 4\pi r^2$
Volume of Sphere	$V = 4\pi r^3/3$

Appendix

Standard Abbreviations

A	ampere		K	kelvin
amu	atomic mass unit		kg	kilogram
atm	atmosphere		lb	pound
Btu	British thermal unit		m	meter
C	coulomb		min	minute
^{o}C	degree Celsius		mph	mile per hour
cal	calorie		N	newton
Ci	curie		Pa	pascal
eV	electron volt		psi	pound per square inch
^{o}F	degree Fahrenheit		rad	radian
ft	foot		rev	revolution
g	gram		s	second
h	hour		T	tesla
hp	horsepower		V	volt
Hz	Hertz		W	watt
in.	inch		Ω	ohm
J	joule			

Prefixes for Powers of Ten

10^{-2}	centi	c		10^{3}	kilo	k
10^{-3}	milli	m		10^{6}	mega	M
10^{-6}	micro	μ		10^{9}	giga	G
10^{-9}	nano	n		10^{12}	tera	T
10^{-12}	pico	p				
10^{-15}	femto	f				

Appendix

Conversion Factors

Time
1 y = 3.16 x 10^7 s
1 day = 86,400 s
1 h = 3600 s

Length
1 in. = 2.54 cm
1 m = 39.37 in. = 3.281 ft
1 ft = 0.3048 m
1 km = 0.621 mile
1 mile = 1.609 km
1 LY = 9.461 x 10^{15} m

Area
1 m^2 = 10.76 ft^2
1 ft^2 = 0.0929 m^2
1 cm^2 = 0.1550 $in.^2$
1 $in.^2$ = 6.452 cm^2

Volume
1 m^3 = 35.32 ft^3
1 ft^3 = 0.02832 m^3
1 liter = 1000 cm^3 = 10^{-3} m^3
1 liter = 1.0576 quart
1 quart = 0.9455 liter

Mass
1 ton (metric) = 1000 kg
1 amu = 1.66 x 10^{-27} kg
1 kg weighs 2.2 lb
454 g weighs 1 lb

Force
1 N = 0.2248 lb
1 lb = 4.448 N

Speed
1 mile/h = 1.609 km/h
1 km/h = 0.6215 mile/h
1 m/s = 3.281 ft/s = 2.237 mile/h
1 mph = 0.447 m/s
1 ft/s = 0.3048 m/s = 0.6818 mile/h

Acceleration
1 m/s^2 = 3.281 ft/s^2
1 ft/s^2 = 0.3048 m/s^2

Energy
1 J = 0.738 ft·lb = 0.2389 cal
1 cal = 4.186 J
1 Btu = 252 cal = 1054 J
1 eV = 1.6 x 10^{-19} J
1 J = 6.241 x 10^{18} eV
1 kWh = 3.60 x 10^6 J
931.43 MeV from mass of 1 amu

Power
1 W = 0.738 ft·lb/s
1 hp = 550 ft·lb/s = 0.746 kW
1 Btu/h = 0.293 W

Pressure
1 atm = 1.013 x 10^5 Pa
1 atm = 14.7 psi = 76.0 cm Hg

Appendix

The Greek Alphabet

Alpha	α	A		Nu	ν	N
Beta	β	B		Xi	ξ	Ξ
Gamma	γ	Γ		Omicron	o	O
Delta	δ	Δ		Pi	π	Π
Epsilon	ε	E		Rho	ρ	P
Zeta	ζ	Z		Sigma	σ	Σ
Eta	η	H		Tau	τ	T
Theta	θ	Θ		Upsilon	υ	Y
Iota	ι	I		Phi	φ	Φ
Kappa	κ	K		Chi	χ	X
Lambda	λ	Λ		Psi	ψ	Ψ
Mu	μ	M		Omega	ω	Ω

Solar System Data

Object	Mass (kg)	Radius (m)	Period (s)	Orbit (m)
Mercury	3.27×10^{23}	2.44×10^6	7.60×10^6	5.79×10^{10}
Venus	4.90×10^{24}	6.05×10^6	1.94×10^7	1.08×10^{11}
Earth	5.98×10^{24}	6.37×10^6	3.16×10^7	1.50×10^{11}
Mars	6.40×10^{23}	3.40×10^6	5.94×10^7	2.28×10^{11}
Jupiter	1.90×10^{27}	7.14×10^7	3.74×10^8	7.78×10^{11}
Saturn	5.64×10^{26}	6.00×10^7	9.30×10^8	1.43×10^{12}
Uranus	8.73×10^{25}	2.62×10^7	2.65×10^9	2.87×10^{12}
Neptune	1.03×10^{26}	2.52×10^7	5.20×10^9	4.50×10^{12}
Pluto	1.5×10^{22}	1.1×10^6	7.85×10^9	5.91×10^{12}
Moon	7.36×10^{22}	1.74×10^6		
Sun	1.99×10^{30}	6.96×10^8		

Earth-Moon Distance $\quad R_{EM} = 3.84 \times 10^8$ m

ANSWERS TO ODD-NUMBERED PROBLEMS

Introduction

1. a) 3.14; b) 23,700; c) 0.556; d) 0.00984
3. a) 6.38; b) 50,200
5. a) 2.17×10^2; b) 5.41×10^{14}
7. 63,400 in.
9. 30.5 cm
11. 2.4×10^7 mm
13. 105 km/h
15. 108 km/h
17. 10,000 cm^2

Chapter 1

1. 789 km/h
3. 3.5 mph
5. 15 mph
7. 50 km/h
9. 9.38×10^8 km
11. 18.6 days
13. $\approx$ 4.4 m/s
15. $\approx$ 2.8 m/s^2
17. 5 mph/min
19. a) 3.56 mph/s; b) 46.4 mph
21. 3 km/h/s south
23. 20,000 mph/s
25. 6 m/s^2
27.

t(s)	v(m/s)	d(m)
0	0	0
1	9.81	4.91
2	18.6	19.6
3	29.4	44.1
4	39.2	78.5

29.

t(s)	v(m/s)	d(m)
0	29.4	0
1	19.6	24.5
2	9.81	39.2
3	0	44.1

31. a) 0; b) 3 s; c) 3 s; d) 44.1 m;
    e) 29.4 m/s
33. 200 m; 250 m
35. 49.6 m
37. 88 ft; 176 ft

Chapter 2

1. $\approx$ 3 N west
3. 66 N at 55° above the horizontal to the left
5. 7200 N east
7. 9.8 m/s^2 to the right
9. 42 kg
11. 4; red
13. 5 s; 10 m/s
15. 15 m/s^2
17. W = 68.7 N; m = 42 kg
19. 824 N + 42 N = 866 N
21. 4 lb
23. 0.8 m/s^2
25. 2.8 N

Chapter 3

1. a) 2 m/s south; b) 2 m/s north; c) 8 m/s north; d) 5.83 m/s at 71.6^o west of north
3. 141 mph southwest; 1.41 mph/s southwest
5. 20 m/s^2; 1600 N
7. 2.74×10^{-3} m/s^2; 1.99×10^{20} N
9. 20 m/s and 5.19 m/s upward
11. 0.48 m
13. a) 2 s; b) 10 m
15. 49.6 m/s
17. a) 1 s; b) 19.6 m
19. 300 N·m

Answers

21. 1.88 rad/s^2 = 0.3 rad/s^2
23. 30 rev/s
25. 125 rev
27. 2.5 rad/s^2
29. 2 kg·m^2

Chapter 4

1. 5.93×10^{-3} m/s^2
3. 2.19×10^{-4} m/s^2
5. 1.63×10^{21} N
7. 5.45×10^{-5} of the sun's
9. The object with the smaller acceleration has 9 times the mass
11. 0.245 N
13. 1.63 times greater
15. Jupiter exerts 11.8 times as much
17. 7.35×10^{22} kg
19. 3 m/s^2
21. 1.62 m/s^2
23. 0.4 g
25. 5.59 km/s
27. 238 min
29. 20,400 km
31. 2.45 N/kg

Chapter 5

1. $p = 60,000$ N·s; $v = 60$ m/s
3. 40 s
5. 16,800 N; 24.5 times
7. 0.51 s
9. 0.12 m/s
11. 4.76 m/s
13. 0.5 m/s left
15. Yes
17. 42,400 kg·m/s northwest
19. 21.4 m/s
21. 22 km/s
23. 1.57 kg·m^2/s

25. 25 rev/min
27. N·s = (kg·m/s^2)·s = kg·m/s

Chapter 6

1. 400 J
3. 14.1 m/s
5. Yes; yes
7. No
9. 6 J
11. 188 N
13. 0.32 J
15. 157 ft
17. 300 J
19. 4320 J
21. 7850 J
23. kg·(m/s)^2 = (kg·m/s^2)·m
25. 7850 J
27. 13.9 m/s
29. 29.4 m/s
31. 62.4 m
33. 1490 W
35. Goes into gravitational potential energy
37. N·m/s = J/s

Chapter 7

1. 10^{-2} cm
3. 1000 m^2; less than half a football field
5. 1.25×10^{16} atoms
7. 3.36×10^3 Pa
9. 3.56×10^{22} molecules/liter
11. -40°C; -17.8°C; 21.1°C
13. -40°F; 89.6°F; 158°F
15. 60°C; 140°F
17. 233 K; 310 K
19. -273°C; 37°C
21. $v_h = 4v_o$
23. 1/3 the absolute temperature
25. 2.55 liters

Answers

27. 1.6 atm
29. 320 balloons

Chapter 8

1. $680 \text{ kg/m}^3 = 0.68 \text{ g/cm}^3$
3. 3890 kg/m^3; 0.707 of earth's density
5. 21.6 g
7. 36.8 cm^3
9. 164 N/m
11. 36.8 cm
13. 1.02 kg
15. $1.47 \times 10^5 \text{ Pa}$
17. 41.2 m
19. $1.01 \times 10^6 \text{ Pa}$
21. $1.18 \times 10^5 \text{ Pa}$
23. 12.8 N
25. $2.04 \times 10^{-5} \text{ m}^3 = 20.4 \text{ cm}^3$
27. $2.7 \times 10^{-3} \text{ m}^3$
29. 73% above the surface

Chapter 9

1. 12 J
3. 1190 cal
5. 0.0179 Cal
7. 0.239 Cal/s
9. $4.19 \times 10^4 \text{ J}$
11. 161°C
13. $0.215 \text{ cal/g·}^{\circ}\text{C}$
15. 49.8°C
17. 20°C
19. 58.8 g
21. 134 kJ = 31.9 kcal
23. 539 cal compared to 80 cal
25. 79.8 g
27. 1650 W
29. 1450 W
31. 7770 nm
33. 500 nm

35. 4.08 cm
37. 1.19 cm
39. 1.0036 liter

Chapter 10

1. 500 J
3. 33.3%
5. 61.7%
7. For nuclear: $Q_{in} = 3.13$ J; $Q_{out} =$ 2.13 J; For coal: $Q_{in} = 2.63$ J; $Q_{out} =$ 1.63 J; the nuclear wastes 30.7% more energy
9. 0.998
11. 27.8
13. 1/5
15. 6
17. 1/12
19. 29k

Chapter 11

1. a) 30 m/s forward; b) 10 m/s backward
3. 50 m/s at 36.9° forward of sideways
5. 220 N
7. 180 N
9. 14 m/s^2
11. 0.102 m
13. $43.8 \text{ m/s}^2 = 4.47$ g
15. $1.71 \times 10^{-2} \text{ m/s}^2$
17. $3.5 \times 10^4 \text{ m/s}$
19. $1.9 \times 10^{-10} \text{ m/s}^2 = 1.93 \times 10^{-11}$ g

Chapter 12

1. 500 s
3. 4.11 h; 0.11 h
5. $\gamma = 2.29$
7. $\gamma = 1.15$
9. 0.99995c
11. 0.966c

13. 0.994c
15. 0.87 m
17. 0.8c
19. 1.03×10^{-18} N·s
21. 1.03×10^{-12} N
23. 8.2×10^{-14} J
25. 0.943c
27. 1.38

Chapter 13

1. $5.82°$ from vertical
3. 2.18×10^{-14} m
5. 2.74×10^2 m/s^2 = 27.9 g

Chapter 14

1. 0.2 s
3. T = 18 s; f = 0.0556 Hz
5. 0.157 s
7. 0.79 N/m
9. 1.27 kg
11. 2.2 s
13. 3.98 m
15. 1.64 m/s^2
17. 5.6 s
19. 4 m/s
21. See Fig. A.1.
23. 1.33 m
25. f = 0.5 Hz; T = 2 s; v = 0.25 m/s
27. (4 m)/n with n odd
29. 1 Hz
31. 0, ±0.5 m, ±1.0 m, ...
33. 3.43 m

Chapter 15

1. 355 m/s
3. 2.72 s
5. 85.8 m
7. 100 dB

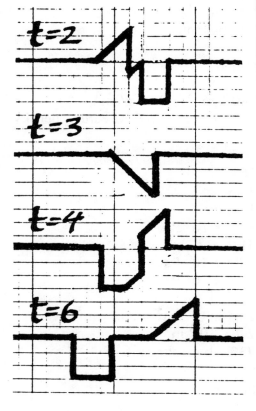

Fig. A.1

9. 2100 Hz
11. 1000 Hz
13. λ_1 = 120 cm; λ_2 = 60 cm; λ_3 = 40 cm
    f_1 = 417 Hz; f_2 = 834 Hz; f_3 = 1250 Hz
15. 343 Hz
17. 172 Hz
19. 4 Hz
21. 552 Hz
23. 146 Hz
25. 478 Hz and 337 Hz

Chapter 16

1. 0.4 m
3. 2 m
5. real; 60 cm in front; -1

Answers

7. 15 cm behind the mirror
9. at infinity
11. 30/23 cm behind the surface
13. $1/s' = 1/(-f) - 1/s < 0 ==>$ virtual
15. 51.7 y
17. 9.47×10^{17} km
19. 1.69×10^{5} y

Chapter 17

1. 6 ft
3. 2.67 cm
5. real; 60 cm on far side; -1
7. 15 cm on near side
9. 20.4 cm
11. 3.33 cm on the near side
13. virtual; 12 cm on near side; 0.6
15. 1.88 mm
17. 1 cm
19. 0.5 m
21. 1.75 cm

Chapter 18

1. 2.29×10^{8} m/s
3. 1.5
5. 5 ns
7. 3.49 mm
9. 560 nm
11. 3.36 cm
13. 0.0437 mm
15. 110 nm
17. m(200 nm) with m an integer
19. 552 nm

Chapter 19

1. 2.12×10^{-6} N
3. 5.09×10^{10} N
5. 9.21×10^{-8} N repulsive; same size but attractive

7. force quadruples
9. force doubles
11. 1.18×10^{21} m/s^2
13. 5.71×10^{13} C
15. 1.25×10^{9} N/C
17. 2.53×10^{28} m/s
19. 75 J
21. 36 J
23. 18 J; -18 J
25. 6,000 V
27. electric potential = electric potential energy/coulomb. Therefore V = J/C and VC = J

Chapter 20

1. 0.0621 Ω
3. 0.588 m
5. 20 Ω; 5 Ω
7. 18 Ω
9. 2 Ω; 4 Ω; 9 Ω; 18 Ω
11. 3 V
13. 2 V and 4 V
15. 1.5 A and 0.5 A
17. 1.5 V
19. 12 V
21.

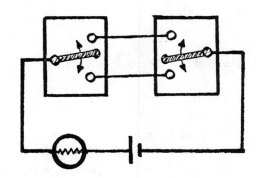

23. 1440 W
25. 13.3 Wh
27. 8¢
29. 18 bulbs

Answers

31. 12 W; twice as much
33. 10W bulb; it has more resistance

Chapter 21

1. 1.92×10^{-14} N
3. 1.42×10^{-6} m
5. 100 turns
7. 30 V
9. 3×10^{10} Hz
11. 5.45×10^{14} Hz
13. 2.48 m
15. 188 m to 556 m

Chapter 22

1. 1.76×10^{11} C/kg
3. 3.65×10^{-19} J
5. 1.51×10^{33} Hz; no
7. 1.51 eV
9. 1.14×10^{15} Hz
11. 2.12×10^{-34} J·s
13. 2.12×10^{-10} m
15. -3.4 eV
17. 3.4 eV
19. ultraviolet
21. 3.28×10^{15} Hz

Chapter 23

1. 0.243 nm
3. 1.05×10^{-34} m
5. 2.87×10^{-11} m
7. 2.41×10^{-17} J = 151 eV
9. 2.41×10^{-9} J = 15.1 GeV; not possible
11. 3.64×10^{5} m/s
13. 3.64×10^{-5} m
15. 0.218 mm
17. 41.4 eV

Chapter 24

1. 3.7×10^{13} decays/s
3. 9.77×10^{16} nuclei
5. 62.5 ng
7. 2 µCi
9. approx. 7 half-lives = 86 y or 6.64 half-lives = 81.7 y
11. 22,900 y
13. 11,500 y
15. 4.5 billion y
17. 1/8
19. 1950 γ/s

Chapter 25

1. 4.14×10^{-6} MeV/c
5. 7.68 MeV/nucleon
7. 169.92 amu
9. 174 MeV
11. 9×10^{19} reactions/s
13. 16.9 g/h
15. 3 g/h
17. 12.9 MeV
19. 4.26×10^{9} kg

Chapter 26

1. 939 MeV
3. 2.27×10^{23} Hz
5. 1.24×10^{-12} m
7. 138 MeV
9. 2.26 fm
11. 0.0136 fm